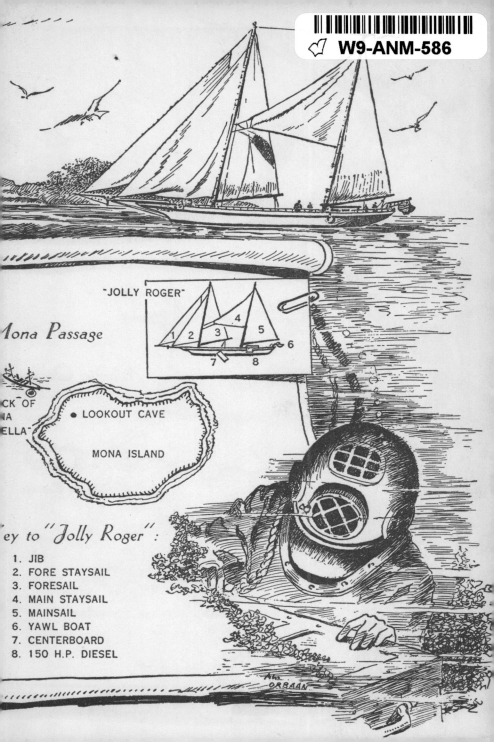

"JOLLY ROGER"

Mona Passage

CK OF
NA
ELLA

• LOOKOUT CAVE

MONA ISLAND

Key to "Jolly Roger":

1. JIB
2. FORE STAYSAIL
3. FORESAIL
4. MAIN STAYSAIL
5. MAINSAIL
6. YAWL BOAT
7. CENTERBOARD
8. 150 H.P. DIESEL

ORBAAN

Treasures in the Depths

other **LODESTAR** *books*

BLAZE BATTLERS
PATROL TO THE KIMBERLEYS
SPACEWARD BOUND

TREASURES
IN THE
DEPTHS

by ROBERT UHL

Prentice-Hall, Inc.   New York

Treasures in the Depths

CHAPTER 1

Excited voices rose from the end of the Mathews dock. A dozen men peered anxiously down at a small barge, on which two worried deckhands were jerking at a heavy line trailing over the side. Now and then someone on the dock shouted a word of advice or instruction, but the general tone was one of confusion, uncertainty and growing horror. Chris and Larry Cahill stopped their aimless strolling and broke off their earnest discussion of their family's future to ask a bystander what was happening.

"There's a man down there—sixty feet down—a diver—."

"Something go wrong?"

"They can't haul him up. The life line must be snagged on something."

Seventeen-year-old Larry looked at once at his brother. Funny that they'd just been discussing diving! Chris, only last week out of the Coast Guard, had been service trained as a deep sea diver, and now that their father's death had left him more or less responsible for the

3

family, he found himself a little worried. Diving was the only trade he knew. He could ship out on a freighter of course, but Mrs. Cahill wouldn't like that any more than she'd like his making his living under water. Besides, they all wanted to stick together if they possibly could— Larry, twenty-year-old Peter, Chris, the eldest, and Mom.

They were clannish; they couldn't be really happy unless they were together. But all they possessed in the world at the moment were their house, a little insurance money, a small pick-up truck and an old work boat that had been their father's. And the desire to stay in Port Hemlock, here on Puget Sound, where they'd lived all their lives.

"Chris, you can help!" Larry exclaimed as the crowd on the dock buzzed with excitement.

"I'm way ahead of you, boy!" Chris put his shoulder to the crowd and started through, with Larry following like a half-back behind his interference.

"I'm a diver," Chris called down to the men on the barge. "Can I help?"

"We need help," came the excited answer. "Hurry up. There's a spare diving dress in the cabin."

Chris jumped to the deck of the barge, with Larry close behind. One of the men dragged out the diving dress and equipment as Chris put crisp questions to the other.

"Who's down there?"

"Sam Dougherty. We can't haul him up—and the phone's out too."

"Is he getting air?" Chris looked at the steadily pulsing compressor.

"Air's okay."

"Stop jerking that line," Chris called to the other topside man as he buckled the weighted belt. "You'll only foul it worse."

He rose and clumped clumsily to the diving platform, Larry trying to help him, only to be brushed aside by Chris. One of the handlers lowered the huge copper and brass helmet over Chris' head and locked it in place. Chris adjusted his air and exhaust valves, checked his sheath knife, snapped a hack saw to his belt, grabbed the shot or descending line, and dropped swiftly out of sight into the murky water. Larry watched anxiously as the air bubbles from his brother's exhaust mingled with those from the imprisoned diver, and shivered as he wondered how it must feel to be trapped ten fathoms down.

Chris descended swiftly. As his eyes adjusted to the dim gray light, he saw a weird tangle of enormous logs, thousands of them, some flat in the mud, some up-ended, some swaying gently in the tide. It was a diver's nightmare. But there was no time to wonder about this sunken jungle. He recognized the other diver who was jammed against a huge hemlock, and signalled for slack.

Sam Dougherty was an old hand. He pointed down, and Chris dropped beneath the tangle of logs and felt for his lines. Apparently Sam had got snagged when he started to rise, and in his effort to free himself, had dislodged several logs which had fallen across the air line. Chris tried to lift one of the waterlogged trees, then saw Dougherty signalling frantically. He adjusted his valve to increase buoyancy and rose to the same level. Placing their helmets together so that they touched, the two divers were able to hear one another.

"Don't move the logs," Dougherty shouted. "That's how I got in trouble. Cut the line."

"Okay. I'll signal them to send down a new air line and life line." Chris did not have a telephone in his helmet. In a short time, the new lines were lowered on a shackle fastened to Chris' descending line. Chris fastened the new life line around the fouled diver's waist, and signalled for air on the new air hose. Soon a stream of bubbles was rushing out of the open end of the hose. Dougherty grabbed the nearest free coupling of his fouled air supply line, and closed his exhaust valve and his air control valve. This left Dougherty only the air inside his dress to breathe. With perfect teamwork, Chris immediately uncoupled the fouled air supply hose and let it dangle as he coupled on the new one. Dougherty was now able to re-open his valves. Chris cut Dougherty's snagged life line, and the diver was free.

The two divers moved back to the descending line, and were hauled up to the decompression stage for their ascent. Back on the barge, they relaxed as they were helped out of their helmets and dress. The spectators on the dock called down congratulations and questions, while Larry watched his older brother, speechless with pride and hero worship.

On the barge, conversation about the incident soon ebbed. Dougherty slapped Chris on the back. "Thanks, pal. Do the same for you, sometime."

"Hope you never have to," Chris answered. "But that is one sweet mess down below. Where do all those logs come from?"

"From the big rafts when the loggers float them down from the camps. Some of the logs—the hemlocks especially—are almost as heavy as water. The air spaces fill up with water, and a lot of them sink."

"Must be a couple of hundred thousand feet of timber down there," said Chris.

"More, most likely. They've been sinking for years. Bad place. I went down for an anchor that came unshackled from a ship. Got a cable on it without trouble, but I should have moved away from the tangle before I told them to haul me up."

There is something sobering in any descent, even a brief dive like this one, and divers are generally quiet men after they've been down. At first Larry plied Chris with excited questions, but when he got only monosyllabic answers, he turned to daydreaming. Larry had decided what his career was to be. He would become a deep sea diver. He was off on an imaginary underwater treasure hunt when Chris suddenly stopped.

"Larry! I've got it."

"Got what?"

"I know how we can make some money. Lumberjacking. Only we'll do it right here in the harbor. Underwater. We'll salvage those sunken logs!"

CHAPTER 2

Salvage the sunken logs. Larry's quick enthusiasm jumped at the idea, and he found it hard to be patient until evening, when they could have a conference with Mrs. Cahill and Peter. Then, at his mother's reaction, his heart sank.

"You know how I feel about deep sea diving, Chris. It's just too dangerous. Besides, what could you dive for here in Port Hemlock?"

"For logs. Hemlock logs that sink right in the bay from the lumber rafts. I saw them when I went down today. They're not deep, and there are thousands and thousands of them. All I have to do is haul them out and deliver them to the Imperial dock right here in town."

"It sounds too easy, Chris. Nothing is that simple. But I'll wait till you've thought it through. I'd rather sell the house and move to the city than stay on here, but—"

She smiled proudly at her three sons. Chris was the kind of person any prospective employer would like, but he had always had a dream of working for himself, of building his own business. He was quietly capable, respon-

8

sible, and with half a chance he would come out with flying colors. Peter's frequent bouts of sickness had kept him from the outdoor life his brothers relished, but had done nothing to diminish his irrepressible optimism. Larry was adventurous and warm-hearted, often in trouble for some thoughtless scrape, but never mean or deceitful.

"Yes, indeed!" Mrs. Cahill said. "If it's important to you and you all want it, and it sounds at all feasible—well, you know I think this is a hard town for a woman to live in, it simply breeds worry!—but—I believe in you all, and I'll let myself be persuaded. You'll have to make a de-tailed plan of course, and there's the question of the money you'd need—"

They shook hands all around; first obstacle con-quered!

Later his brothers pumped Chris for details of his plan. Peter was wholeheartedly in favor of it. The ad-venturous aspects appealed so to Larry's imagination that he could think of nothing else. Chris was reticent about his specific plans, but under prodding, he began to talk about deep sea diving, in which he had been trained while in the Coast Guard and which had become a deep-seated passion with him.

Among the odd, dangerous and romantic professions of our modern world, that of the deep sea diver is prob-ably the one most obscured by misinformation, miscon-ception, and sheer ignorance. A deep sea diver invades an uncharted world; he sees sights man was never meant to see; his occupation is one of the world's most hazardous; he looks like an invader from another planet. It is inevita-ble that generations of romancers should spin elaborate fantasies until the deep sea diver of fiction no longer bears much resemblance to his flesh-and-blood contemporary. Mention the word "diver," and most people think of sunken ships with long-dead pirates still sprawled about a rum puncheon—Spanish galleons—treasure chests waiting to be stumbled upon—exquisite coral reefs populated with rainbow-hued fish—wolf packs of sharks and barracuda that must be fought off with knife and bare hands—mysterious dark caverns tenanted by the nightmarish octopus or fearsome morays—vistas of unearthly beauty—and always, everywhere, the spice of unknown dangers that drain the last resources of human strength and courage.

There is just enough truth in this picture to keep the legends alive. Man has completely tamed his environment on land; the trackless oceans are his highways; he is gradually mastering the earth's atmosphere. But he is still nibbling at the edges of the great area beneath the sea—an area totalling 70 per cent of the earth's surface. The sea hides immeasurable wealth, treasure that makes the imagination swim. Over half the world's *minted* gold and silver lies there, without counting precious ore. The extent of oil and mineral wealth can scarcely be guessed, while subsurface plant and animal life will inevitably prove of tremendous value in a crowded world whose population is still multiplying and whose known resources are dwindling at a terrifying rate.

But the diver himself—the man to whom these wonders are an everyday experience—shows no external evidence of adventurousness. The diver who is a ready talker or who encourages acquaintanceship is apt to be a rarity, for the man who descends under the sea is conditioned by his own peculiar world, the weird, dimly lighted depths which are as unlike the earth as the planet Saturn.

Larry and Peter, still excited by Chris' almost poetic (for him) description of deep sea diving, spent the night in dreams of wildest adventure. Chris' thoughts were more prosaic, but they kept him awake as long. They could

form a salvage corporation. Peter and Larry were smart
enough to handle the topside work; Mrs. Cahill could take
care of papers and records; he could dive. There should
be a second diver, though. Sam Dougherty's close call that
very day proved that it would be too dangerous to dive
alone. A second diver below—or ready to go down if
needed—should reduce the risk of serious accident. Chris
wondered if Sam Dougherty would be willing to work
with him on shares. Mentally, Chris computed the cost of
the equipment he would need, and the changes necessary
in the *Chinook*, his father's work boat, to make it adequate. Most of all, Chris wondered where he could borrow
the considerable sum of money he would need to make his
dream a reality. He had little to offer in the way of secur-
ity, except a lifelong reputation in the town for honesty
and industry. How much would a bank loan on a reputation? Chris didn't know, but he meant to find out. Better
still, to offer some more businesslike collateral along with
the reputation—if only he could get it.

CHAPTER 3

Next morning, Peter and Larry were subjected to an inspection by Chris as rigid as any they'd ever endured as youngsters. After much debate, Chris had decided that they should make the projected call on the lumber company officials as a group, since the others would be as deeply involved as he. Chris wanted Mrs. Cahill to come, too, but she declined. She still had doubts about her consent to Chris' scheme.

The boys had their first lesson in big business when a secretary told them that they couldn't see Mr. Norton, the branch manager. He was too busy, and anyway, the big boss, Mr. Anderson, was momentarily expected. Everyone would be tied up as long as Mr. Anderson was in town.

Convinced that his scheme was practical and profitable for all concerned, his plans all laid, Chris couldn't endure delay.

"All right, then," he told the secretary, "if everyone is so busy worrying about Mr. Anderson, I'll see Mr. Anderson himself."

"Oh, you can't do that," said the secretary, visibly shocked. "Mr. Anderson is a very big man." Then, as an officious young man came out of an inner office and strode importantly past the desk, the secretary said: "Mr. Creighton, these young men wanted to see Mr. Norton and when I told them he was too busy, they said they would see Mr. Anderson!" To the Cahills, the secretary explained: "Mr. Creighton is Mr. Norton's chief assistant."

"You want to see Mr. *Anderson?*" demanded the chief assistant incredulously. "You can't see Mr. Anderson. He's a big man, a very big man. He's the *President*."

Chris' mouth became grim, and his chin jutted. Any man *that* big ought to be diminished a little.

"Look," he said. "I'm not trying to be unreasonable. If I can't see Mr. Anderson or Mr. Norton right now, when can I see them? I'll wait. Surely your whole business doesn't close down just because the president of the company pays a visit. I'll bet he wouldn't like it if it did."

There came a sudden interruption from behind the group. "That's the smartest remark I've heard today," said one of several men who had just entered. "My name is Anderson, and if you've got business with me or with Mr. Norton that's important, go right ahead. But please don't waste our time if it's not important, because the young lady is quite right. We *are* busy."

"How many feet of timber do your raft booms drop to the bottom of the Sound every day, Mr. Norton?" asked Chris.

"Thousands of feet. It's a chronic problem. Why?"

"For every sunken log, you have to cut another tree and float it down the Sound?"

"That's right."

"Suppose I can haul those logs out of the Sound and deliver them here at your dock. Interested?"

"Interested."

"How far will that interest go financially?"

Mr. Norton looked inquiringly at Mr. Anderson. "It's up to you, Norton," Anderson said.

"Can we be sure these people can do it?" asked Creighton doubtfully. "They look pretty young, especially these two," nodding toward Peter and Larry. "This sounds like a tall order for three full-grown men. Do you think teen-agers can solve a problem as stubborn as this?"

"My teen-agers are better qualified to create problems than to solve them," remarked one of the men who had come in with Anderson and Norton. "All I seem to read or hear about these days is the trouble caused by teen-agers. Their behavior is a public disgrace."

This was too much for Larry Cahill. "Why is it," he demanded, "whenever some kid gets in trouble, everyone starts yelling that teen-agers are no good? I don't see any headlines that say, 'Gang of thirtyish hoodlums hold up store'; and the radio doesn't say 'Raid discloses middle-agers' dope ring.' Do people complain when teen-agers donate blood, or help put out forest fires? Everybody tells us to judge people as individuals, but they don't judge kids from twelve to twenty as individuals. We're teen-agers, and we're no good!"

Larry stopped from sheer lack of breath. Chris and Peter unconsciously moved closer to him, as if to repel an attack. There was no attack. Instead, Mr. Anderson boomed with approving laughter.

"You're dead right, young man. And I like your spirit." Mr. Anderson didn't look at all formidable right now. "Answer the young man's question, Norton," he concluded. "How much will you pay for the logs?"

Norton turned to Chris. "We'll pay you sixty percent of the original value of the logs."

"Will you put that in a contract?" asked Chris.

"We'll give you a contract saying that, and we'll

agree to take all the logs you can deliver, with one proviso. The timber must be sound."

On the strength of the contract with the Imperial Pulp and Paper Company, the obvious earnestness of Chris, and the excellent reputation of the Cahill family, the bank gave them the financing they needed. The Port Hemlock Marine Salvage Corporation was in business.

In a wild flurry of activity and excitement, Chris located some diving gear from the War Assets Administration, bought an old diesel-powered steel crane barge, and three compressors or air pumps. Sam Dougherty gladly joined up as the second diver, and began to teach Peter and Larry their topside duties.

The diver's topside man or tender must keep his wits about him. Sam gave Peter and Larry careful instruction. Of course, the diver, either Chris or Sam himself, would be in constant telephone communication with topside, but most divers rely as much as possible on hand signals on the line. Telephones can go out, but the hand line is almost foolproof. They learned the simple signals:

Tender to Diver

1 pull: Are you all right? (or—"Stop") if diver is ascending or descending.
2 pulls: You are too far up; go back down till I stop you.
3 pulls: Stand by to come up.
4 pulls: Come up.

Diver to Tender

1 pull: I am all right.
2 pulls: Give me slack.
3 pulls: Take up slack.
4 pulls: Haul me up.
3 pulls, then 2: More air.

4 pulls, then 3: Less air.

5 pulls: Send me a line.

Emergency Signals—Diver to Tender

2-2-2 pulls: I am fouled. Send another diver.

3-3-3 pulls: I am fouled, but can clear myself.

4-4-4 pulls: Get me out of here!

Interpreting hand signals can be a tricky business, Sam told them. All slack must be taken up until the tender can feel the diver on the other end. Yet the lines must not be so taut that they pull the diver away from his work or even yank him off balance. The proper signal is a gentle but distinct pull. All signals by either tender or diver are repeated when received, to show that they are understood. Failure to repeat a signal means that it is not understood.

Sam warned the boys against yanking in too much line when giving signal pulls; against leaving slack line when the diver is descending. They would have to keep track of the diver's bubbles and keep the line taut enough to get signals at all times. If the bubbles disappear for a moment or two, or if they stay in one place instead of moving about as the diver moves, he must be checked at once to see if he is all right. The tender must be careful to keep the engine exhaust to leeward of the compressor intake, and to change the position of the compressor if necessary because of wind shifts. Several divers have died from inhalation of carbon monoxide poisoning, the result of inexperienced or inattentive tenders who placed the compressor intake too close to the engine exhaust. Power boats had to be kept clear of the diving area, and, most important, they had to keep track of the time and depth of the dive, so they could decompress the diver properly during the ascent.

"A good tender 'feels' the diver at his work," Sam told them. "He develops an uncanny sense of what is going on under the surface. The tender should be able to tell almost instantly when the diver is in trouble."

Both boys nodded seriously, and Sam drove the point home with an incident from his own experience. "We were diving for scrap steel on a wrecked vessel. This was during the war, when steel was short. A clamshell bucket would bite into the heap of scrap and hoist a load to the surface. The bucket wasn't working right, and I went over to investigate. In shifting around, my hose and line got tangled with the bucket's block. When the winch began to haul it up, I felt my air hose go taut. My life line was all twisted in the cable." Sam paused a moment and stared at the horizon as the horror of that moment came back to him.

"Sixty feet to the surface, and the water like blue ink!" Sam finally continued. "I had no phone, the air supply could hardly sustain me, and I couldn't signal with the fouled line. If my tender had chosen to raise the bucket, the air line would have snapped, and that would have been the end of Sam Dougherty." He paused again.

"What happened? How'd you get out?" demanded Larry.

"I had a good tender. Without quite knowing why, he had a feeling he ought to ease the tension on the clam shell. He did, and I was able to unknit my tangled lines." Sam looked keenly into the eyes of Peter and Larry Cahill. "That's the kind of tender Chris and I want you boys to be."

In a matter of weeks, diving operations were underway. The whole bottom of the Bay was covered with logs, and recovering them was almost ridiculously easy—too easy, Mrs. Cahill felt.

CHAPTER *4*

〰〰〰〰〰〰〰〰〰〰〰〰〰〰〰〰〰〰〰〰〰〰〰〰〰〰〰

Initial salvage operations were begun right in the Bay, for speed and convenience. The water was shallow—most of it not over seventy to ninety feet (or twelve to fifteen fathoms, as the Cahill boys spoke of it as their nautical vocabulary increased).

Chris did most of the diving, with Sam Dougherty supervising topside operations. The logs were three to four feet in diameter, and around forty feet long. Chris would grope along on the murky bottom till he found a couple of particularly big logs, and then shackle them together, continuing till he had twenty-eight logs, which was a capacity load for the Crane barge. Then he would ascend, and the crew would go to work hauling them up. After each dive, Larry would query Chris about conditions on the bottom, and ask when he would be allowed to make a trial dive. Larry was gradually building up a considerable knowledge of diving—secondhand information, of course, but he knew that sooner or later, Chris would feel more like talking than he did right after a dive. And that sooner or later, Chris would let him go down too.

18

It was a proud day when the Cahills prepared to deliver their first load of salvaged timber to the Imperial Pulp and Paper Corporation. Mr. Norton himself came down to greet them and to inspect the logs. He was beaming.

"There you are, Mr. Norton," said Chris. "First load on our contract—138 logs. It should come to almost $2,000."

"Fine! Splendid! Let's take a look at them."

"Right," said Chris. "I picked out the biggest logs I could find—grandpas, all of them. Look at this one."

"Hmmm," said Mr. Norton, inspecting the log closely. He looked unhappy. "Hmmm," he said again, and prodded another log.

"Something wrong?" asked Chris anxiously.

"Teredos."

"Come again?"

"Teredos," explained Mr. Norton. "Underwater wood borers. Shipworms. They've chewed this log hollow . . ."

"No good?" asked Chris, his heart sinking.

"I'm afraid not. Not for pulp. We can't use it."

"What about this one?"

"Same thing," said Mr. Norton. "See these little white marks on the bark? That's a sure sign. Skeletons of the teredo slugs. This one is bad, too."

"What about this?" asked Chris, getting panicky.

"Let's see. Hmm. That one may be all right. But the one under it is bad . . . and that one . . . that one."

"Most of them, then . . ." said Chris.

"It looks that way. But unload them all from the scow. I'll have one of my inspectors go over the lot. When we have it, we'll send you the report."

The Cahills were learning that it takes more to get a business started than just the idea . . . even more than the push to see it through. You need to learn that little thing called "know-how." Chris had a long talk with the inspector. He would have to learn to grade the logs underwater—not just to locate them. It would slow him up —how much so he couldn't yet tell.

The teredo or shipworm has been a scourge to seafaring men since time immemorial. Ships' bottoms are protected against it by poisonous bottom paint or by metal sheathing. In unprotected wood the teredo larva settles on the wood, scrapes a hole, and disappears below the surface. The worm has a siphon which clings to the surface, and it actually grows longer as it eats its way into the wood fiber. When the siphons are withdrawn from the small entrance burrow, the opening is blocked by a pair of paddle-shaped plates of shell. These small white spots were the signs Chris had to look for to determine whether or not a log was worth salvaging.

The next evening, as the Cahill boys were walking home, Chris stopped without explanation in front of a house with an M.D. sign outside. "Be a good idea to have you checked over," he said to Larry, who looked at his brother as if he were crazy.

"What for?" he demanded. "I haven't been sick a day since I had the measles four years ago."

Complaining humorously, Larry let himself be led into the doctor's office, while Peter, who knew what it was all about, continued home.

"You're the healthiest looking patients I've seen in a year," the doctor greeted them, looking at their bronzed faces. "What can I do for you?"

"This young fellow thinks he'd like to explore the bottom of the bay in diving dress," said Chris. "Would you check him over, especially his ears, heart and lungs?"

Larry passed his physical examination with honors. At last he was going to dive! He was already schooled in such fundamentals as operating the air supply and exhaust valves and other instruments, some of which are located in the helmet and worked with the diver's chin. As ordered by Chris, Larry had a light breakfast, and he told Chris he had had a good night's sleep, which was a slight exaggeration. He had been too excited to sleep.

First, he got into a suit of woolen underwear, and donned a pair of heavy wool socks. These were not only for warmth, but also to prevent chafing from the stiff diving dress (Larry had long since learned that it is always called a diving "dress," never "suit"). Next he was helped into the diving dress, made of a layer of India rubber between layers of heavy twill. Chris laced the backs of his legs to prevent air pressure from ballooning them out and upsetting him. Larry was then seated on a stool, and his copper-and-lead-soled shoes were put on. These weighed 17½ pounds each. Next came the helmet cushion, followed by the breastplate. Carefully, to avoid tearing, Chris pulled up the rubber collar and placed it over the projecting studs—Larry raising his arms to make it easier, like a young child being dressed by his mother. Washers went over the studs, breastplate straps were put in place, and screwed tight with wing nuts. A wide belt, weighted with eighty-three pounds of lead slugs, was strapped around his waist. Then he stood up and bent forward while the crotch strap was adjusted to keep the helmet from floating off his head.

While Chris was helping Larry get dressed, Sam Dougherty had been checking the diving helmet, testing the valves and telephone, and coupling up the necessary length of air supply hose. Larry was now wearing 136 pounds, and he needed help as he staggered to the edge of the barge and descended the ladder a few rungs to the diving stage. A safety line was snapped on, to prevent an accident such as once befell an absent-minded commercial diver who forgot his helmet was off, and stepped away from the ladder.

Chris now lowered the fifty-four-pound copper and brass helmet over Larry's head. Like every neophyte, Larry looked up at the eerie contraption as it hovered over his face. If there was any claustrophobia in his system, it would come out now! The helmet had heavy glass ports or windows in front, on each side, and also on top so that he could look upward without having to lean backward. A diver can't turn the helmet, but can turn his head inside it. Outside, on the right side of the helmet in easy reach of the diver's hand, is the regulating exhaust valve, with which he adjusts the escape of air to suit his needs. This is in addition to the automatic air escape. The telephone transmitter and receiver are inside the helmet, the wires being encased inside the life line.

Chris lowered the helmet with the faceplate open over Larry's head, and screwed it into place. The safety catch was turned down into its recess, the recess closed by a hinged stopgap, and a split securing pin inserted to avoid any chance of the helmet accidentally coming loose. The combination telephone and life line was then drawn under his right arm and right front of the breastplate, and the air hose drawn under his left arm and fastened. The air supply pump was started, and Chris told him to test his telephone, air valves and other instruments. When he quavered "okay," Chris gave him a last warning: "Take it easy. We'll let you down slowly so you'll have time to get accustomed to everything."

The faceplate was closed, and Larry grinned back at the others watching him. He closed the air regulating exhaust valve and then reopened it the proper number of turns for ventilation and buoyancy. It was time now to descend.

There was a continuous noise in Larry's ears—a combination of the hiss of air entering his helmet and the roar as it escaped through the valve. In his nostrils was the smell of rubber and metal polish. The compressed air had a stale taste, like the air from an automobile tire. His first sensation was the pressure of the water driving the air from the lower to the upper part of his dress, forcing the dress against his body. Larry watched to see the water close over the faceplate. There it was, a thin green line! He released the breath he hadn't realized he had been holding all this time. His ears felt clogged. He swallowed, and his ears opened up with a POP. All he could see was the column of air bubbles trailing up from the exhaust valve.

The first few minutes on the way down, Larry found himself breathing too hard. Gradually he got used to the pressure. He wondered if Peter and the others topside tending his line had their minds and hearts on their job. This was no time for them to be stargazing. They were mighty important guys to Larry right then.

With his leg around the descending line, Larry tried to keep his back to the tidal current, so that he would be forced against his descending line and not away from it. His ears started to hurt, so he stopped his descent and "popped" his ears by pressing his nose against the wall of the helmet to close his nostrils, and making a strong effort to exhale. The pain disappeared as pressure inside his ears was equalized. Then he was at the bottom. Holding on to his descending line for a moment, he looked around him curiously, but even in the bright light of his underwater torch, he couldn't see well. Everything looked hazy. This was a fairly deep dive, for indoctrination, not for work. Gradually, Larry found his senses becoming dulled. His throat was dry from swallowing to open his ears, and he felt queer, as if he had taken a narcotic. The simplest task became strenuous, as he discovered when he located a log and tried to move it. He remembered that he must com-

municate constantly with those topside through his telephone, so they wouldn't begin to worry. Larry hoped his
comments were brisk and intelligent, but actually his voice
through the telephone sounded to those above like
Mickey Mouse. His nose itched, but there was nothing to
do but endure the itch. The diving dress was not unduly
cumbersome, but Larry found it hard to coordinate his
movements. Following instructions, he adjusted the supply
and exhaust of the air until first he was light and buoy-
ant and floated off the bottom, and then he was heavy and
could lie or crawl on the bottom. His dress caught in some
unseen obstruction, and in momentary terror he yanked
himself free. Then he reflected that he had been sternly
warned not to try to jerk himself loose, but to use his
hands slowly and deliberately, finding the snag and releas-
ing it gently, lest he tear his dress.

Suddenly Larry felt a suspicious dampness. Yes—
there was water *in* the dress with him! A leak! His voice
was shrill with panic as he called the barge on his telephone. Bubbles streamed past his faceplate, and not only
from the exhaust valve. Chris and Sam could tell on the
barge that Larry was scared. When a diver is breathing
normally, the air bubbles come up in a steady stream.
When he gets rattled, they come up in clusters—and big.
"Don't get excited," said Chris stoically on top. "Tell us
when the water gets up to your chin." For one hysterical
moment, Larry thought they were going to let him drown.
He didn't know that Chris was deliberately testing him,
to see if he would go into a complete funk.

Actually a small leak in a diving dress is nothing to
get excited about. The air pressure will keep the water
from climbing to the strangulation point. And since Larry
had invaded a world where things have been wet since
creation, it would have been unfair for him to escape in
complete dryness. But he was cold, and he'd had enough.

He moved over to his descending line and asked to come up. It seemed an endless trip.

With one leg hooked around the descending line, and his hand on the regulating exhaust valve, he started up at a rate of twenty-five feet a minute. A weighted diving stage had been fastened to his descending line with a sliding shackle. Chris' voice over the telephone warned him when he was coming close to it. There it was. Larry inflated his dress slightly to increase buoyancy and lighten himself, mounted the stage, and sat down. He phoned Chris: "On the stage," so they could start timing the first stop in his decompression.

As he rose and the pressure dropped, moisture condensed and fogged the faceplate. Suddenly he felt himself begin to float above the stage, and hurriedly he adjusted the exhaust valve, which must be changed to allow for the reduced pressure. At long last the stage came to the surface and he stepped off to the ladder, climbing till he was only waist-deep in the water. Chris snapped on the safety line and then he and Sam helped Larry, who was now feeling the weight of the 190 pounds of equipment he was carrying, to clamber aboard. The helmet was removed and Larry grinned with self-conscious pride as he realized it wasn't so bad after all, though he found that he did have a headache and felt a little edgy despite his sense of triumph. Larry could understand now why Chris seldom felt talkative after a dive.

Sam Dougherty clapped Larry heartily on the shoulder, and remarked to Chris, "Guess you won't be needing me any longer, now you've got Larry here all broken in." He said it with a smile but there was an undercurrent of seriousness in Sam's tone that made both Chris and Peter look at him soberly.

"Getting restless, Sam?" asked Chris.

Sam looked a little sheepish. "You know me, Chris.

The original rolling stone. I can only stick to one job so long. This one looks like a long haul for short profit."

"Anything definite in mind?"

"Well, yes," answered Sam. "Got an inquiry the other day from an old friend. They're looking for divers at Casablanca."

"What's doing there?"

"British transport sunk during the war. Had the payroll for the whole expeditionary force. Good job. Thirty-five dollars a day plus all expenses, plus a buck extra for every foot you do down below sixty feet." Sam paused a moment. "They need more divers, Chris."

"No thanks," said Chris.

"Thirty-five bucks a day—no maybes, no worries," coaxed Sam.

"And no future," Chris interrupted him. "Nothing you can sink your fist into and hold on to. It's not the money. It's being on my own . . . my own boss . . . taking my risks . . . taking my profits . . ."

"And your losses," reminded Sam.

"That's right," answered Chris. "That's part of the deal. But it's worth the gamble. When you've got a business, your own business, you can grow. You're not stuck under water. You can get up . . . on dry land. I'm sticking with this, Sam, as long as I'm able to. I'm going to see it through."

Larry and Peter, who had listened aghast to this debate, breathed sighs of relief. A lot of other dreams would burst if Chris gave up his.

"Can you stick by us a while longer till I get things rolling a little?" Chris asked.

"Of course, Chris, of course," said Sam, his face red with embarrassment. "I didn't mean I'd desert you when you're in a pickle. We can train Larry for relief diver right on the job, and Peter is already a good topside man."

"I think Larry has the makings of a diver, Sam, but you and I aren't going to train him. We just don't have the time or the knowledge. If we can just get a little money ahead, Larry's going to the Sparling School of Deep Sea Diving!"

CHAPTER 5

〰〰〰〰〰〰〰〰〰〰〰〰〰〰〰〰〰〰〰

For a time, things went
smoothly. Chris was becoming more and more accurate
in grading logs on the bottom of the Bay. Gradually, they
were extending their operations out toward the Sound.
Chris let Larry make a couple of dives in the Bay, but forbade him to go down in the swift currents and colder,
deeper waters of Puget Sound. Peter had become fairly
expert at topside management, and Sam Dougherty stayed
loyally at work, though often there was a faraway look
in his eyes that told the brothers Sam's restlessness had not
subsided. When they tallied up accounts at the end of the
month, Mrs. Cahill announced that the Port Hemlock
Marine Salvage Company had paid all current bills, and
had a bank balance of $902.33.

"That two dollar and thirty three cents is your bonus,
Mother," said Chris. "Go blow it in on a fur coat or something. Live a little."

They all laughed, but they all, without mentioning it,
remembered that the bank loan was still to be paid when

it came due. Mrs. Cahill had something else on her mind, and she was dead serious about it.

"Chris, Mrs. Maynard says that you've seen sharks when you were under water, and an octopus, too. I want a frank answer. Is that true?"

Chris looked accusingly at Peter and Larry, to see who had blabbed. Larry blushed. Despite their conspiracy to avoid mention of any incident of their operations which might alarm their mother, Larry had been unable to resist telling some of his friends about their adventures. He hadn't exactly falsified them, but he certainly had not minimized their encounters with other living creatures under the water. As a matter of fact, there were not just occasional sharks, there were a lot of them, and other fish too. There was not just one encounter with an octopus—there were many. Octopuses, in fact, were a downright nuisance.

Chris tried to explain to his mother. If the creatures of the deep were as dangerous as writers paint them, few men would become divers, and they would not survive for long. Sharks, for example, may nose around, but Chris told her that all of the divers he had talked with were unanimous that in most waters, they don't attack. He told how during the Spanish-American War, the Navy store ship *McPherson*, deep-laden with beef, went on the rocks on the north coast of Cuba. Divers were sent down to patch her damaged plates while the deck crew jettisoned tons of decaying beef to lighten her. Sharks by the hundreds appeared, ripping and tearing at the carcasses of beef, fighting among themselves, churning the water into bloody froth. For days the divers braved this maelstrom of maddened sharks, yet not one attack was made.

There have been divers so contemptuous and daring that they have kicked inquisitive sharks in the belly and gotten away with it. Others have slapped big sharks away, and bare-skin divers have hitched-hiked rides by clinging to a shark's tail. This form of playfulness, Chris reassured his mother, he had never gone in for. The biggest shark they had seen was a five footer, and a punch in the snout had sent him about his business. They weren't like the giant tiger sharks of the South Seas. He demanded to know if she had ever heard of an attack on a human by a shark in Puget Sound.

How about the octopus? The cold malignancy of its small, oval, slanting eyes and the snake-like movement of its tentacles give it an appearance of devilishness which belies its timid nature. Divers agree that it is seldom dangerous to a man in a diving dress if he keeps his wits about him. Stand still, and a curious tentacle will usually be withdrawn. Never will it jet *toward* a diver or any other creature that might do it harm. Chris told them that the only attack he knew about was on a diver who came across a "small" octopus feeding on snails. The diver let fly a vicious kick, whereupon the octopus unwound into a fourteen foot specimen who naturally tried to take the diver into camp, though with the help of another diver and topside personnel, he was able to escape without difficulty. "In this case," said Chris, "you must admit that the octopus had provocation."

It would be an exaggeration to say that Mrs. Cahill's fears were entirely quieted by Chris' speech on marine zoology, but it was true that she had never heard of any serious trouble with either sharks or octopuses in or around Port Hemlock.

The proposal that the infant business' small cash reserve should be used to send Larry to the Sparling School of Deep Sea Diving, in Wilmington, California, brought fresh distress to Mrs. Cahill. Chris had become used to treating Larry and Peter as responsible adults, and they had both lived up to this treatment. But Mrs. Cahill had a longer perspective. Always worried about Peter's precarious health, she remembered vividly Larry's harum scarum days, which, in truth, were not entirely behind him. She thought he was too young and irresponsible for a calling as inherently dangerous as deep sea diving. But, as Chris pointed out, they couldn't expect to hold Sam Dougherty indefinitely; Larry was already making some dives; the Sparling School had a record of over 30,000 man hours of diving without a single accident, and, as far as could be determined, none of the thousand graduates of the school had ever been seriously injured while diving. With proper training, which the school could supply; with good equipment and common sense, for which Chris would make himself responsible, diving can be done safely. And, Chris told his mother, never before in history have divers been in such demand, or paid so highly. As a final argument, Chris reminded her that, sooner or later, Larry would have to serve a hitch in the Armed Services. His training at the Sparling School would probably provide him with grade, pay, privileges and opportunity to learn much greater than he could hope for otherwise.

The decision was made. Larry was to go to the Sparling School, and since a new term was about to start, he was to leave at once.

CHAPTER 6

~~~~~~

It was with mixed emotions that Larry left for Wilmington. The prospect of attending the famous Sparling School, the only civilian school of deep sea diving in the world, was exciting. It was an adventure to travel alone so far from home—farther than he had ever been. But he felt a sense of guilt at leaving Chris and the Port Hemlock enterprise while affairs were still in such a precarious state; and he hated to see the first hard-won profit from their joint efforts spent entirely on him. On this score, Chris reassured him that his expenses at school represented a re-investment of profits by their business in expectation of a greater return at a later date—a policy that every business, great or small, must follow if it is to grow.

Larry fingered the envelope containing his medical report, and hoped that he would pass. Diving is one of the most rigorous occupations in the world. You need great physical strength and endurance. You can't be more than 12 per cent overweight. Fatty tissue absorbs more of the dangerous nitrogen from the compressed air than muscle or sinew. You must be at least five feet four inches tall, and not more than six feet four inches, or the apparatus, which comes in standard sizes, will not fit you. A quiet, unexcitable person is less likely to develop compressed air illness than the nervous type. When you're excited, you use up twice as much air. Quick, accurate judgment and initiative and above average intelligence are essential.

Vision defects which are correctable are no problem, although you should wear contact lenses instead of regular eyeglasses. Any evidence of pulmonary disease makes diving unwise, because high atmospheric pressure has an irritant effect on the lungs. Middle ear disease is disqualifying, because this prevents rapid equalization of pressure. Any chronic disorder of the respiratory system unfits a man for diving. The decompression tables are based upon normal functioning of the heart and lungs. A big chest expansion helps, as it gives you more lung power.

Mechanical aptitude is very important, since commercial diving is really nothing but underwater mechanics. Educational background requirements are not formal, but the candidate should know elementary physics (pressures, displacement, buoyancy, laws of gases, etc.) and must have or acquire familiarity with welding and pneumatic tools.

Wilmington, the home of the Sparling School, is a mariner's town, and its friendliness made Larry feel at home. He reported to the main school building on Wilmington Boulevard, an impressively modern structure with a dummy clothed in full diving dress standing in the window. Larry was one of thirty young men enrolling for the sixteen weeks course. His only misgiving came when he handed over the $600 tuition check. That $600 was more than just money to Chris and Peter and himself. It was a pledge to future independence, and Larry pledged himself to make the most of his opportunity.

They were all a clean-cut bunch of boys, and while

most came from maritime communities scattered along
the Atlantic, Pacific and Gulf Coasts, a few were from the
Great Lakes area, and there were a half dozen or so from
foreign countries. Larry took an instinctive liking for one
lad, a small, wiry, dark-haired boy about eighteen, with a
ready smile and a mischievous twinkle in his eye. His name
was Kevin Morton, he told Larry; he was from Chicago,
and his father and older brother were Lake pilots. Conversation
was general among the student-divers as they
waited, with one burly chap with a loud, harsh voice dominating
the group. He let it be known constantly and in
detail that he had already had some underwater experience.
Noticing that Kevin and some of the others in the
group were a bit scornful about this man, whose name was
Max Gsovski, Larry decided that he would keep quiet about
his own limited experience.

The first meeting with the instructors was inspiring,
more because of the background of these men than because
of anything they said. Lt. Cross, the Director of the
School, had a history which any man would envy. Born
in the state of Washington, he teamed up at fifteen with a
group of barnstorming pilots, with dreams of becoming
a wingwalker. Later he spent a summer hunting and fishing
with an Indian tribe, followed by a spell of wild horse
breaking. Wanting to see the world, his next step was the
Navy. In 1934 he made his first dive, beginning a career
which has included work on the great sunken liner *Normandie*,
a dive to a depth of 240 feet in Lake Tahoe at an
elevation of over one mile; an underwater metal-cutting
job in Canada in four feet of water under three feet of
ice; inspection of Roosevelt Dam, eighty feet underwater
inside a 150 foot tunnel. He had been Flag Secretary to
the Commander of the Salvage Unit at Bikini during the
Atom Bomb tests.

Lt. Cross had a hard look—not hard-boiled, but

tough and enduring. His smile was pleasant and came easily, but it was a tight, controlled smile, like all his expres-
sions and motions. One got the impression that here was a
man who was completely master of himself and of any
circumstance in which he might place himself.

Lt. Cross' welcoming talk was brief and to-the-point,
without verbose preliminaries. He told the new men of
the pressure test and the elimination dive, which deter-
mines whether or not they are physically and psychologi-
cally suited for a diving career. He warned them that
some of them would surely fail one or both of those tests
and that only about half of most classes successfully passed
the course. Larry was not the only member of the class
whose face grew serious at this warning.

The other members of the School's staff were almost
as inspiring as Cross himself. Lt. Mihalowski was the oldest and most experienced. He had been a diver for almost
twenty-five years, had helped in the development of modern decompression tables and oxy-helium diving. He had
been diving instructor at the U. S. Naval Academy, at the
Navy Salvage School; was Salvage Officer at Pearl Harbor, Okinawa and Yokosuka; and like Lt. Cross, had par-
ticipated in "Operations Crossroads." Larry noticed with
a thrill that Lt. Mihalowski wore in his lapel the miniature
ribbon of the Congressional Medal of Honor, the result of
his work in helping to rescue thirty-three men from the
ill-fated submarine *Squalus*, sunk in 240 feet of water.

Then there was Mr. Hamby, who specialized in salvage and construction diving and had been a diver since
1938 and a Master Diver since 1944; Mr. Adam, a graduate
engineer from the University of Wisconsin, who among
other subjects taught explosives and rigging; and Mr. Mol-
nar, youngest of the group, son of a famous commercial
diver, a former Navy diver and honor graduate from the
advanced course at the Sparling School. An exceptionally

skilled welder, some of his test plates tested the highest ever attained in underwater welding.

Larry and Kevin found the tour of the main School building and inspection of the equipment fascinating. Besides the classrooms and the set-ups for learning rigging, welding, and cutting above water, the recompression chamber and the various shops, there was a special training tank set up so that nine divers could be accommodated at one time, each working at a different underwater technique—such as carpentry, welding, burning—with underwater portholes from which the instructor could see and correct the student's mistakes before undesirable techniques might become a habit. A speaker system permitted the instructor and the student to communicate with each other as work progressed.

The pressure test constituted the first of the elimination procedures. The students entered the School's Recompression Chamber in small groups, to determine their reaction to the high air pressures encountered in diving. The recompression chamber was a large cylinder of heavy steel, with benches inside, and a circular air-tight door. Pressures up to fifty pounds per square inch were gradually applied. At the thirty, forty and fifty pound levels, each student was required to write a paragraph. In addition, he was required to perform a mathematical problem at fifty pounds pressure.

Larry found that performance of these simple requirements was far more difficult than at atmospheric pressures, but he felt reasonably confident that his showing would be satisfactory. Some of the students apparently found it tough going, and when they emerged from the chamber to meet the critical stares of the instructors and answer their searching questions as they probed for signs of excessive nervousness, it was apparent that, although some had failed, Larry and Kevin had passed.

The plump lad who had sat next to Kevin was in some distress. He complained of a thick, cold, "lumpish" feeling and considerable pain in his right shoulder and was placed back in the chamber with one of the instructors for additional decompression. He left school that day.

The School lost no time in debunking popular superstitions about the dangers of diving, because it was essential that the students should learn not to fear things that were unlikely to threaten their safety, yet to recognize and know how to confront the dangers that are real.

The genuine romance of the diver's calling has seldom been translated into print without distortion. Whenever a man places himself in an unnatural environment, certain inherent hazards are present. None of the flights of the fiction writer could exaggerate the dangers of diving, but the flesh-and-blood diver faces problems more serious than the sharks, morays and octopuses that writers love to dwell upon.

As far as can be determined from available medical records, no authentic case is recorded of serious injury to a diver in American waters by shark, octopus, or moray eel. No doubt deaths have happened, but they must be rare or they'd show up in the records. The Army's "frog men" in World War II came in frequent contact with sharks, barracuda, eels, rays and octopuses, but there were no serious tussles with any of them. However, many marine creatures will fight if cornered, and due respect must be given for their ability to inflict damage—usually by tearing the dress. Even snapping turtles can make trouble this way. But while they can cause bad scares and mild injury, casualties by animate enemies are so unlikely as to be lightly dismissed by most divers. They regard these creatures of formidable reputation as everyday passers-by in the deep. Even such perils as the "bends," the "squeeze," or poisoning from oxygen or carbon dioxide are being eliminated by thorough training and supervision.

The one implacable enemy of the diver, they learned, more dangerous than all the vicious creatures in all the oceans, is the staggering weight of the water in which he works. Modern equipment enables the diver to match the strength of this enemy, but it is always there waiting. He cannot conquer it, cannot eliminate it. He invades Neptune's territory under an armed and uneasy truce.

For every thirty-three feet you descend under water, another atmosphere of pressure is added on your body— roughly equivalent to 14.7 tons. Air must be fed to the diver at thirty-five to fifty pounds pressure above that of the water in which he is working to counteract this pressure and provide proper ventilation of the helmet. If the air supply should be cut off, the tremendous pressure of the water would collapse the suit and ram the diver into his copper helmet like a hydraulic press. This is called a "squeeze," and it is a terrible death. The body is completely mashed, and loses all semblance of humanity. Flesh may be stripped from the bones, and tissue even extruded into the air line. Divers say of a bad squeeze: "Only thing left to do is to bury the helmet."

The sheer horror of the squeeze has caused it to be magnified in the minds of outsiders. Slight cases occur whenever the air pressure in the diver's helmet is allowed to fall below the pressure of the surrounding water. This can happen not only from failure of the air supply or a rupture of the air hose, but also from the diver falling a considerable distance. In the past fifteen years, since the development of the helmet safety check valve, there have been no serious cases of squeeze. The check valve automatically closes when the air flow is cut off, and the exhaust valve does likewise, leaving the diver with such air as the suit contains. If he is working in shallow water, he then has about ten minutes to reach the surface before succumbing to the carbon dioxide of his own exhalations. In deeper water, the time is much shorter—only about one minute at 280 feet even with a well-ventilated helmet.

Another hazard of diving which has largely been conquered is caisson disease, commonly known as the "bends." At high pressure, the nitrogen in the air dissolves in the blood stream and collects in the joints and the blood vessels. When the air pressure is reduced, the nitrogen is released, but a sudden release would have the same effect as opening a soda bottle. The nitrogen forms bubbles which rise and press on nerves, or block veins, causing severe contraction of the muscles, bleeding from nose and mouth, convulsions, and occasionally paralysis or death. Gradual surfacing, which gives the body a chance to decompress naturally, removes any danger of the "bends." In the past five years there have been approximately twenty-five cases of "bends" in the Southern California area. All were successfully treated with no permanent ill effects to the diver.

If in an emergency a diver must surface in a hurry, he is stripped by his helpers of his dress and rushed to a decompression chamber. There the pressure is quickly built up according to the time and depth at which the diver has been working, then gradually reduced. This hazard, however, can be practically eliminated by using an artificial atmosphere made up of helium and oxygen instead of nitrogen and oxygen. Helium is only half as soluble as nitrogen, and it diffuses (that is, leaves the blood stream) at twice the rate, so the danger of large bubbles in the arteries is practically eliminated. Unfortunately, use of helium-oxygen is expensive, although not nearly so much so as a few years ago. It is not needed in depths under eighty feet, where most commercial diving is done, but it opens new possibilities for deep offshore oil drilling and salvage of sunken ships and cargo.

The use of helium also reduces the danger of oxygen poisoning. The dissolving of the nitrogen in the concentrated air leaves an excessive amount of oxygen. At 250 feet, the oxygen pressure in the air is the same as breathing pure oxygen at 1.8 atmosphere gage. Safe tolerance on air at this depth is only about forty-five minutes. The longest decompression table for 250 feet is fifty minutes and requires 299 minutes for ascent. In its milder form, an oxygen jag is like intoxication, but since it fogs the diver's mind, it can lead to mistakes that may cause a fatality. The diver can make only one major mistake, and he gets no second chance. Severe cases of oxygen poisoning have effects similar to pneumonia. Helium carries away body heat rapidly, so that a diver working on helium must wear electrically heated underwear. But he can work many times longer at great depth, and work more effectively, than on compressed air. This is a tremendous advantage, for only the time at work counts, and normally a man can make only one deep dive in twenty-four hours. It takes that much time for all of the nitrogen to pass out of his system.

It is possible for a diver's air control valve to freeze, especially when submerged in very cold water. Cooling of the air causes moisture to condense and form droplets on anything it touches. Furthermore, the air comes to the diver's air control valve at high pressure and then pressure is reduced, with a resulting expansion and cooling of the air. Condensation is deposited on the sides of the air control valve, and if it freezes, it builds up, layer by layer, until the valve is blocked by a plug of ice.

A more common accident, and one which has claimed several lives, is fouling—wrapping of the life line and air-hose around an object, either by incautious movement by the diver, action of currents, or movement of the object on which he is working. Failure of the air supply results in suffocation. Or the opposite can happen. If the air exhaust valve fails, the air pumped from above can bloat the dress until the diver dangles in the water like a four-pointed starfish, limbs outstretched, and is unable to use the life and death gadgets in the helmet. His only hope then is that he will balloon quickly to the surface, where his predicament will be revealed to his tenders, before the dress bursts.

Currents present a major hazard in some waters. Currents are the winds of the sea bottom. Sometimes barely perceptible, at other times and places, they may be irresistibly strong, sweeping before them loose objects like divers or even huge ships. The students were warned to tread carefully when these "breezes" are blowing hard.

CHAPTER 7

~~~~~~

After five days of preliminary instruction came the first tank-dive . . . the "elimination" dive. This was more a psychological test than anything else. The students were dressed in full deep sea equipment, descended in the training tank, and performed a number of evaluation tests designed to determine their reaction to specific orders. A couple of students who showed extreme excitement and talkativeness were advised to take up some other line of work. A diver's life will often depend upon calm thinking and sound decisions, and an emotional person is too likely to make mistakes.

Thanks to their genuine interest, Larry and Kevin passed this test without difficulty. Then began a long, tough grind, most of it practical work, during which Larry and the other students learned every phase of diving technique in different types of conditions and waters. They studied basic physics, learned how to prevent and how to treat occupational diseases, practiced the fundamentals of boat operation. They had to become expert in the use of scores of hand and power tools, acquire a sufficient knowledge of ship construction and repairs—in fact, they became expert in a dozen trades besides diving. Since the simplest jobs become difficult under water, training began with such elementary tasks as tieing knots and building wooden boxes. Larry and Kevin both made the classic mistake of putting down a piece of wood on the bottom, forgetting that gravity doesn't always work. When they let go, the wood shot up to the surface like an arrow. Most hated chore was mud-tunneling, but often the only practical way to raise a sunken ship is to burrow through the slime to place a cable under the ship's bottom.

Gradually Larry became so thoroughly accustomed to his new element that he could take his mind off the fact that he was in diving dress. His reactions to the adjustments of his air supply and exhaust became automatic. Working in pitch dark, he was learning to concentrate on the job to be done, get and keep a mental picture of everything below, and then feel his way around like a blind man.

During the second semester, the students left the sheltered training tank to dive in open water, first from the barge and then from the school power boat. Descending to 100-foot depths in murky water, with unseen objects fouling their lines and mysterious arms clutching at their legs was a marked change from the calm water of the diving tank.

The barge was moved out into the ocean so they could study jetting, air lift, the use of pontoons, underwater rigging, and block and tackle and chain falls. They learned how to locate and inspect a sunken vessel, and what to do after the inspection. It was all practical work, with definite assignments for each dive.

Larry wrote home faithfully. One letter read: "We have our own forms of playfulness. One is to 'go fishing' —with a hook and line, not a spear. This pastime has advantages over the conventional sport, since the fish are there with you in plain view, and you are equally visible to them. If a fish won't come to the hook, you take the hook to him. If he fails to bite, you can snag him. But unlike the above-water angler, who hopes for the biggest fish in those waters, we've got to content ourselves with a small specimen. In his own element, the fish fights so effectively that it's extremely difficult to take him off the hook —almost impossible with a big fish. Only difficulty is that the School doesn't go for this kind of fishing. Not sporting. I guess they're right. Another stunt we do is to break up a small shellfish and hold it out to the fish. Whole schools will swarm in and eat from your hand provided you make no sudden movements.

"The old hands here in Wilmington claim that a man can be buckled into his diving dress, handed an apple, submerge, and come up with the core in his hand. The trick is for the diver to bend over so that his helmet points down. He then turns the air pressure on full force, opens the front window of his helmet, and calmly eats the apple. The air rushing out against the water is supposed to keep it from entering the helmet. After the apple is eaten, the diver closes his faceplate, reduces the air pressure to normal, and goes topside with the apple core clutched in his hand. The only trouble with this story is that while I have heard half a dozen outside divers swear they have done it, or knew men who had, I could never persuade anyone to demonstrate it in my presence. And when I asked Lt. Cross about it, he laughed and winked and asked me what I thought. I told him I guessed that was one trick I'd skip.

"You'll remember, Chris, that after my first trip down, I was disappointed at the darkness and gloom. I thought when I got to Southern California I'd find a clean sand bottom, clear water and lovely scenery. 'Tain't so. It's more like strolling around in a bottle of ink.

"We do a lot of diving in pairs—something like the

'buddy system' in the Army. We talk to one another without telephones by getting a foot or less apart. It's easiest if you put your helmets or breastplates together, so the vibration is transmitted from one helmet to the other. When I first went down with another diver, I kept thinking I was bumping into a post, but all the time it was the other diver.

"I got awful wet today. I'd always heard that you can scare off over-inquisitive fish by opening a wrist cuff and 'shooting' a stream of air bubbles at the fish. I found out that the released air cannot be 'shot'; the bubbles rise straight up just as they do from the exhaust valve. It's the sudden motion that frightens the fish, not the bubbles. All I accomplished was to let some mighty cold water get into the dress with me."

In another letter, Larry wrote: "We had an exciting experience today. I had come up from a deep dive—280 feet—and my helmet had just been removed. One of the other students, Kevin Morton, was still down, finishing his assignment with a jackhammer. He was talking over the telephone, and his conversation was as normal as anyone could expect at that depth. He said his faceplate had steamed up, and he was going to wash it off so he could find a starfish for his girl friend. The darned fool closed his air control valve! Almost instantaneously his voice was slurred and unintelligible. In less than thirty seconds he was unconscious. The instructor clapped my helmet back on and I went over, as they started to bring him slowly to the surface. I met Kevin at 125 feet and opened his valves. He didn't regain consciousness for 5½ minutes after proper helmet ventilation was restored. We were then at about 65 feet. When he came to, believe it or not, he was still talking about starfish! He didn't even know he had passed out.

"You sure have to be a mechanic to pass this course!

At first, I had a hard time using any tool under water—even a hammer. The first time I tried to take a timber to the bottom, I had an awful time. Every law of balance and gravity is reversed. The timber seemed to come alive, and with a mighty nasty disposition.

"Putting five slabs of wood together to form a box, all cut to fit, sounds easy. But it's black as Hades down there. It takes minutes to drive a nail. The wooden pieces cooperate by trying to leap out of your grasp. You start by kneeling on the bottom board, starting the nails in each of the side pieces, and go at it with an oversized hammer you carry in your belt. As soon as I reached for the hammer, one of the sides got away from me, but I caught it just in time. The force of the hammer blow is taken up by the water, and the sledge is wilder than Mom tacking down the hall rug. Some of the guys took thirty minutes to put their boxes together. It didn't take me quite that long, but I didn't set any speed records, either. I don't know if I should tell you the dumbest thing I did when I got to the bottom. I didn't seem to have enough hands. So I did just what I'd do on a carpenter job at home. I tried to put the nails in my mouth!

"Well I'm past that kid stuff now! I'm using three kinds of torches—an oxy-hydrogen cutting torch, an electric arc welder, and an oxy-electric cutting torch. Then there's a cement gun for grouting work; tools for pipe bonding, rivet expanding and removing, jet nozzles for mud-tunneling (that's an ugly job!) and lots more. No offense, Chris, but underwater logging seems awfully simple to me now.

"By the way, I told Lt. Cross about our Port Hemlock operation, and he was very much interested. He says that there are other divers doing the same thing in the Coeur d'Alene Lake area. But don't start worrying about competition yet, Chris. Lt. Cross says there's twenty to thirty years work for ten to fifteen divers in that area alone!

"I've picked up all sorts of odd information. Did you know that the history of diving goes back to ancient times? Or that Cleopatra played a trick on Mark Antony once when he was fishing, and had a diver put dead fish on his hook? That gives me an idea. I'm going to have fun with the Port Hemlock fishermen when I get home. I'm going to hook fish on some guys' lines, and take 'em off certain other guys' hooks!

"Grand as all this is, folks, I can't wait to get back to see you all and work with you again. I should be a real help now. Mom, stop worrying about me. The food is fine (though not as good as yours). I haven't caught cold yet; and I'm not carousing around nights in the big city. Divers don't go in much for that stuff—though Lt. Cross told us about a diver he knew when he was working on the *Normandie*. This diver went out on New Year's Eve, acquired a fine hangover, and missed out completely on his night's sleep. When he went down next day, he carefully adjusted his air balance to perfect buoyancy, then fell sound asleep for three hours, mattressed by the North River. Unfortunately, he snored, and his commanding officer heard him over the telephone. That was the end of his diving career.

"So long, folks. Three more weeks and I'll be home. Tell that to the bank if they start pressing you on the loan, Chris."

CHAPTER *8*

~~~~~~

            In Port Hemlock, a light northwest breeze dotted the Bay with ripples. Heat waves danced over the white sand of the dunes, and above the pine-clad hills to westward cumulus clouds were piling up to the zenith. At nightfall, the wind gave a dying gasp, leaving the surface of the Bay smooth as oiled water. Soon a blue-black darkness settled; the water took on a slaty gray tone. Yet still there was nothing to indicate that this was more than a summer thunderstorm.

            The weather men knew better. Transpacific airline pilots studied their weather maps anxiously, and altered their flight plans. Shipmasters whose vessels were close to the coast debated a change in course and speed. Storm warnings hung listlessly from Coast Guard masts. The radio and television carried the alarms—but only for those who could see or hear them.

            Chris could not. Trying to ignore the perspiration dripping down his face, and his sweating hands, he persisted in his efforts to repair a leaking exhaust valve on a secondhand deep sea diving helmet. Chris was working against time, ignoring the clock. He had not read a paper or listened to a radio for days.

Long before dawn the wind blew in from the southwest, a bit south of the very entrance to Port Hemlock. The high tide, made higher by the low barometric pressure, was swelled further by the direction of the strengthening wind which heaped the sea inshore. The surf beat on the beach, while out in the middle of Puget Sound there was a lot more water than usual, most of it standing up on end.

The rising treble of the storm wind broke through Chris Cahill's concentration on his task. Men who earn their livelihood in, on or under the water have a sixth sense about the weather. Even before he got outdoors, Chris knew that this was no ordinary storm. And he had a special reason for anxiety. Anchored near the entrance to the Bay, in open water, was his rickety old diving barge. It would have to be moved. Even as he turned toward the telephone, its bell rang. It was Sam Dougherty, a fellow diver who was working for him as much for gratitude as for expectation of profit.

"Get moving, Chris," was Sam's quick message. "I'll meet you at the dock."

The two divers brushed aside warnings from the other boatmen who were clustered at the dock doubling their mooring lines or gazing anxiously out at their anchored craft from the lee of the watchman's shed. Heavy seas breaking against the pier had set even that heavy structure to vibrating; and the boats and lighters made fast along it ground against one another and against the pilings.

Chris started the diesel engine in the work boat and let it warm up while Sam singled up the mooring lines. Chris set the engine in gear to relieve the strain on the bow line, which one of the bystanders released and tossed on the deck. Sam hurriedly cleared the decks of loose gear and line, to be sure nothing was washed overboard to foul the propeller.

The inappropriately named *Chinook* struggled valiantly against the pounding seas, tossing spray high in the air while solid water engulfed the bows and crashed against the windshield. *Chinook* had a displacement hull, and her propeller was deep enough to keep from breaking the surface—for the moment at least. A fast, shallow, planing hull would have been helpless against those moving walls of water.

Chris, at the wheel, had difficulty seeing through the streaming windshield. Periodically Sam popped his head from behind the shelter cabin to check the course and nearness to the wallowing barge. Blinded by the hard-driven spume, he had to duck back to clear his eyes.

They could see astern, and the sight was one to shake their courage. Some of the small boats anchored by defective moorings in the bay were swept away quickly. Others held till the high tide caused them to pick up their mushroom anchors and drag toward the eastern end of the Bay where lay in wait a bridge used by the lumber trains, low enough to shear off cabin trunks like a guillotine and to lop off the rigging of the boats swept against it. Soon it was so jammed with wreckage that no victim of the storm could get through. Before the *Chinook* had fought her way alongside the barge, the Bay was swept clean or nearly so.

"Take the wheel, Sam, and see if you can hold us broadside to the barge," said Chris. "I'm going to jump."

"Don't try it, Chris," pleaded Sam, thoroughly frightened at the way the barge bucked and wallowed in the crashing seas.

"We can do it. Gun the engine when she heels toward

us. Don't get too close—you'll have to get clear before
the next roll. Whatever you do, don't hit her."

Chris started to jump for the shrouds on the barge's
derrick, but held back at the last moment as the *Chinook*
rolled away from her. Sam was having difficulty holding
close alongside when he throttled down. Each time he
gunned the engine, the *Chinook* crept a little farther forward on the barge where it would be most dangerous for
Chris to jump. Breathing a prayer, Sam let the *Chinook's*
bow sag toward the barge, then put the wheel over hard
and opened the throttle. The wash from the *Chinook's*
big propeller against the rudder forced the stern over, and
Chris made a flying leap for the shrouds as the barge
dipped toward him. Small broken strands of rusty wire
on the barge's heavy shrouds—"meat-hooks," sailors call
them—tore his palms, and he was ducked entirely under
water by the roll of the barge. But he hung on, and clambered aboard when the barge rolled in the opposite direction. He flashed a quick look at the *Chinook*, which had
rolled to her beam ends, but Sam got her back under
control.

The square-bowed barge was held by two heavy anchors, one in each bow. The cables led out from the rigid
hawsepipes, and the barge plunged into the oncoming
seas and shook them off as she lifted. Along these chains
came the jerky vibration of dragging anchors. Crouched
at the capstan, sheltered in part from the blast by the
break of the forward deckhouse, Chris sensed these vi-
brations through the deck and the soles of his feet. He
fought open a door and grasped a ready coiled lead line
to gauge the drift. The lead line stretched forward. Time
was short!

Chris struggled with the heavy wire towing bridle and
the biggest manila hawser aboard. The wire towing line

would be too heavy for them to pick up from the *Chinook*. Drenched in solid water every time the barge dipped her bows, and in hard driven spray when she rose, Chris buoyed the end of the hawser, dropped it overside, and was paying it out with almost superhuman strength when there was a heavy crash. The huge cargo boom had come adrift from its nest, and was swinging on its gooseneck pivot on the derrick mast. That boom was almost as big in girth as a man. One touch from it would crush anything in its path. The guy lines kept its swing just clear of Chris' position, but if the barge's motion snapped the boom lashings, it would be only a matter of moments before the guy lines carried away.

Sam began edging in with the *Chinook* the moment the boom came adrift, and Chris could only hope the hawser wouldn't foul as it paid out. He knocked the anchor chains loose from the pawls with a heavy sledge, crawling on the deck to stay clear of the swinging boom. Then, as the *Chinook* came abreast, Chris clutched the light line he had made fast to the eye of the hawser, and made a flying leap. He fell in a huddled bundle on the *Chinook's* afterdeck.

When he had collected himself, he belayed the end of the line, and crawled into the shelter cabin.

"Thought you were a goner then, boy," yelled Sam. "What do we do now? We can't maneuver the barge, even if we could pick up the hawser."

"We have to try, Sam," answered Chris. "Here goes."

The *Chinook* almost went over as Sam put about. Chris hauled at the light line, but his strength was nearly gone. Barge and boat were racing downwind when Sam, seeing Chris' exhaustion, recklessly let go the wheel, caught Chris by the shoulder, and thrust him into the cabin. Chris grasped the wheel just in time to prevent a yaw. The two craft slowly separated as Sam hauled on the line, brought the hawser eye to the counter, and with one last surge of strength got it aboard and over the towing bitts.

The only hope of saving the barge was to edge it toward a small point of land that jutted from the shoreline inside the Bay, cut it loose, and let it beach itself in the relatively calmer waters. But it didn't look as if the *Chinook* herself would survive long enough to reach the point. As the relentless combers swept up astern, the *Chinook* tried to rise to them. Then the weight of the towing cable and heavy barge would snub her, and the sea would wash aboard. Even with every deck opening sealed, she was taking in water fast. Chris threw in the clutch on the engine-driven bilge pump, and Sam began to operate the emergency hand pump.

After desperate minutes the *Chinook's* pounding heavy duty engine succeeded in dragging the barge around to a slight angle to the seas. The barge rolled even more wildly now. Then, as both men instinctively held their breaths, the port guys on the barge's cargo boom let go. The boom swung far back to port as the vessel rolled, then over with irresistible force against the starboard guys. They parted as if they were strings.

The boom, swinging pendulum fashion against the leverage of the tall derrick, increased the roll of the barge. Each bulwark in turn dipped under. Then, as Chris and Sam waited for her to recover, there was a long moment of near stability. The barge was not rolling back. The cargo boom was now far out over the water, and the whole starboard side of the deck began to submerge.

"She's going over," yelled Sam in sudden panic. "She'll drag us down. The axe! Where's the axe?"

"In the locker. Quick, cut that line!"

Sam swung wildly at the taut hawser, missed, hit it and cut one strand, cut another, then saw the third strand part from the strain.

The barge lay for a moment on its side, then was gone in a swirl of water and air bubbles which were instantly blown away.

"It's gone," said Sam, almost unbelievingly.

"Sunk," answered Chris. "Everything we have—the whole works—sunk with it. Our business is back where it started, on the bottom of Puget Sound!"

By early morning, the storm had subsided. On the still-swirling, foam-flecked surface the signs of wreckage —oil, flotsam, equipment—churned in the commotion of the water. Only symbols of the fleet were left, often still tied to the vessel below: life rings, hatch covers, skiffs, rafts, flag poles.

A lesser man would have been beaten. But the successful fight to save the *Chinook*, which had made the point in the nick of time, with only minor damage, had revived the courage and determination which had caused Chris to embark on his risky enterprise. He would need help, of course, but he wasn't going to lose for lack of trying.

CHAPTER 9

〜〜〜〜〜〜〜〜〜〜〜〜〜〜〜〜〜〜〜〜〜〜〜〜〜

Before the wreckage of the big storm that sank the Cahills' crane barge had scattered, Larry was on his way home. Port Hemlock was too unimportant a town to be mentioned in the regular press, but the marine newspapers had more complete details. "A marine salvage barge sunk at Port Hemlock" could mean only *their* barge—there was no other salvage barge in the town.

Lt. Cross was away, and would be gone for several days, and Larry could not wait. He wrote a brief message of explanation, packed his belongings, and set out for the bus terminal, determined to help in the family crisis. He was bitterly disappointed at having to leave the school only three weeks from his graduation, and he regretted his inability to take leave properly from Lt. Cross, who had shown such a friendly personal interest in him and in the Cahills' enterprise. But such things, he thought, were unimportant compared to Chris' situation. All the way up to the Sound he worried about whether Chris would be able to resume operations. So much planning and effort had gone into the timber salvage project that it was heart-breaking to think that everything might be lost.

Peter and his mother were glad to see Larry back. Not so Chris. "We invested a lot of money so you could learn to be a rounded diver, with all the latest techniques," Chris said. "Now you miss the last stages of your training, when you would have learned those techniques. I know your motives were good, but it was the wrong decision, Larry."

"Look at it this way," Larry argued, "I *have* learned mud-tunneling and jetting and using pontoons. Sure, there's still a lot I don't know. I'm not being cocky. But Sam Dougherty was getting ready to quit even before I went to school. How's he feel now?"

"We can't hold him much longer," admitted Chris.

"Can you afford to hire another diver?"

"I can't afford to, but I'd have managed somehow."

"How?" asked Larry. "You told me yourself you'd only worked on one mud-tunneling job in the Coast Guard, and that was with a whole crew of divers. You say our only hope is to raise the barge right away. Every minute and every dollar is important. I can go back to the school later and finish up. I'm sure Lt. Cross will understand."

Chris grinned and clapped Larry across the shoulder. "I suppose I'd have done the same thing myself. And I hope you really did learn something about mud-tunneling, because I expect that's the way we'll have to work."

There was something else that came first, however. Their bank loan would be due before their most optimistic chance of raising the barge and delivering the timber to the Imperial Pulp and Paper Company. Chris, Peter and Larry went to see the banker, Mr. Evans.

Mr. Evans listened attentively to their troubles, scratched his nose a bit, then said:

"How much of an extension will you need, Mr. Cahill?"

"One month," Chris said.

"Will that be time enough for you to get rolling again?"

"I want a month. If I'm not rolling by then, I'll be ready to call it quits."

"One month," said the banker. "Let's see—that will be till May 10th. Okay. The bank will go along with you. And . . . good luck!"

Encouraged by this preliminary success, the three brothers went to see Mr. Norton at Imperial Pulp and Paper. He had some bad news for them—something they hadn't figured on. He told it to them straight.

"There's another outfit moving in, Chris. They've approached us for a contract."

"Well, I guess we can't stop that," said Chris. "We have no patent on the idea. It's a good idea, and it stands to reason that someone else would take a crack at it. Do they get the contract?"

"They haven't got it yet," replied Mr. Norton.

"Why not?"

"Well," smiled Mr. Norton, "I'm kind of rooting for your side, Chris."

"We appreciate that, Mr. Norton."

"But just remember, I'm not the man who makes all the decisions around here. I can hold out, but not indefinitely."

"How much longer?" asked Chris.

"Maybe a month."

"Until May 10th?"

"Just about that long. But no longer," said Mr. Norton.

"May 10th—we make a delivery of sound timber on or before that date, or—" Chris paused.

"Or what?"

"Or expect a postcard from me. I'll be off to Casablanca."

Peter and Larry added their thanks to Chris'. "One thing I don't understand, Mr. Norton," said Larry. "I've always heard that big business was pretty tough, yet here's Imperial Pulp and Paper going out of its way to help a little outfit like ours."

Mr. Norton looked pleased. "A lot of people have wrong ideas about big companies, Larry," he said. "Big business needs little business. It couldn't exist without it. The average big corporation helps create and support far more small outfits than it hurts. Big businesses can do certain things better or more economically than small ones. You'll find the big companies anxious to give you every sensible chance, just as we have, and just as the bank did when it extended your loan. But we can't be silly about it, either. If your business isn't going to work out, the sooner you find out and turn to something else, the better it will be for all of you. But I think you can do it."

The Cahills said goodbye to Sam with real regret. They couldn't blame him. He had worked hard and loyally long after he had really wanted to move on, and his lack of faith now was in itself an adequate reason. There would be no room for doubts or pessimism if they were going to get that barge up in time. They couldn't afford to hire professional help on the job, but Mrs. Cahill managed to scrape up enough cash to hire a couple of old barges, some pontoons and cables, and jet equipment.

The first job was to locate the wreck. Chris and Larry laid out a regular search pattern. This was done in circular patterns using a distance line running from the weighted descending line, so that the diver would know how much of the bottom he had covered. Larry went down first, took his distance line over to the leeward side

of the descending line as far as he was able to see. With the
distance line coiled in one hand and held tight in the
other, he swept around in a large circle. When he got
back to the place where he had started, he let out some
more of the distance line, and then made another, wider
circle, this time moving in the opposite direction to avoid
twisting his air hose and life line around the descending
line.

Larry and Chris had to move the *Chinook* three
times, but then they found the barge, and to their delight
discovered that she hadn't capsized completely. When she
went over on her side, the water had poured into her deck
openings, but as she sank she had righted herself, and was
resting on her bottom, though at an angle. Then they
made a fearful discovery. The sea bottom was deep, soft
mud, and while the bow was almost buried in it, the stern
was resting shakily on a solid rock outcrop. They had expected to face the unpleasant chore of burrowing a tunnel
to get lifting cables under her, but they hadn't expected
soft mud under an insecurely balanced hulk. And there
was a fierce current on the bottom except at the change
of tides.

While the rented compressors were stuttering a
working pressure into the reservoir, Chris and Larry argued over the division of work. Finally, they tossed for
sides. Larry won the seaward side, which meant, as the
barge was tilted, that he would have the easy job of inspecting the port, or uppermost side. Chris would tackle
the starboard side, where the deckhouses, guy lines and
other gear and equipment had to be clambered over, with
danger of fouled lines or a torn dress. However, Larry
would have to drive most of the tunnel.

Larry was determined that he would uphold his end
of the assignment. He checked the stern. Sure enough, it
was resting precariously on rock, but there did not seem

to be any damage to the steel hull. He moved forward, downhill, into the deepening water until he was abreast the forward deckhouse. A thin stream of bubbles came from some air lock in the barge, and from that spot forward the hull was sunk deep into the mud. There wasn't the slightest chance of passing a messenger wire under the hull without a tunnel.

Larry and Chris surfaced to talk things over.

"The water looked dark and soupy as I worked down the side," said Larry. "I wonder why."

Chris looked disturbed. "That shouldn't be," he said. "This is slack tide. There's no current to stir things up down there—and no wind up here, though it looks as if a bit of a blow is coming up. See the heavy clouds over on the horizon? Say, do you suppose the barge is still settling? Did you feel any vibration, or hear any noise?"

"No," said Larry. "Suppose I go down again and check?"

"I'll go," said Chris.

"No, it's on my side," said Larry. "If we keep changing sides, we'll be arguing over who is to do each operation. Let's stick to our agreement. Anything on the port side is mine; the starboard side is yours. You've got the worst of the bargain—with all those obstructions on deck to foul you. It'll only take me a few minutes."

Larry went down the shot line again. He moved aft on the hulk, and this time he stopped his exhaust valve for a moment to hear better. At first there was nothing. Then there came a creaking, grinding sound from aft, where the steel plates rested on the rock. At the same time, he became aware of a prolonged vibration through the hull. The bow of the barge unquestionably was gradually sinking deeper into the mud, and, as the angle of the hull increased, probably sliding off the rock. Chris phoned him to surface before the storm broke, as the *Chinook* had only a light anchor down.

As Larry started to work back under the *Chinook*, he noticed a great cloud of mud along her anchor chain. The storm must have struck. The *Chinook* was dragging her anchor. He'd better get up. A little frightened, he hurried toward the shot line. He couldn't find it! It's easy to get momentarily lost underwater, but usually not hard to orient yourself again if you don't panic.

Fear is truly the diver's greatest peril. Not the constant awareness of danger, nor the complete aloneness, nor the butterfly stomach that most men feel before a deep dive, but the fear of fear itself—the kind of fear loosed by real disaster underwater. Larry was afraid of becoming afraid, that in the conflict of emotions his judgment might become poor.

He signaled to be taken up, then thought of the big reef toward which the boat was drifting, and told the crew to drop him back.

"Chris," he said, "the *Chinook's* anchor is dragging."

"I know. Come up."

"Wait," pleaded Larry. "I'm close to a big reef behind the one the barge is on, and the *Chinook* is dragging that way. Suppose I hit against it before I get up? Start the engine to take some of the strain off the anchor till I find the shot line."

There was a pause, and then Chris said, "Larry, we're having trouble starting the engine. You'd better chance it and come up."

But Larry knew he was close to the reef, which was not nearly high enough to harm the *Chinook*, but which was high enough for him to be smashed or scraped against, possibly tearing his dress. For a thoughtless moment he wondered if he could get a line around a big boulder not

far away, to hold the *Chinook*. He couldn't use his air
hose or life line, of course—he had only about one and a
half times the depth of the water in hose, so it would rise
almost straight up, and the first heavy swell against the
full displacement of the boat—over ten tons—would snap
his lines. He couldn't find a new line in time if one were
dropped from the *Chinook*, since he had lost the drop line
and wasn't directly under the boat. He looked again at the
cloud of mud where the anchor was dragging. One fluke
showed briefly—it was backwards! The anchor chain had
fouled around the flukes and stock, and the anchor was
being dragged backwards. He groped toward it, waited
till it pulled slowly past so that it wouldn't catch his dress.
Then he stooped, caught one fluke, and flipped it. That
cleared one turn of the chain. He tried again, moving with
the anchor as it slowly dragged on the bottom. It was hard
to see just how the anchor was fouled because of the
mud. He phoned Chris: "The anchor's fouled. If you can
give me a little slack, I think I can clear it."

"Stay clear," ordered Chris. "You'll get fouled yourself. Besides we've only got about thirty feet of chain
left."

"I'm behind the anchor," replied Larry. "If you can
pay out the chain so it stops moving, I think I can flip it.
I'll keep clear."

"You'll have to work fast," said Chris. "Here goes."

The anchor stopped dragging as the chain was slowly
paid out, but the cloud of mud dissipated slowly. Chris
stooped down and peered at the anchor. There was a single turn of the chain over the curved flukes, near the
shank. He tried to lift the anchor, but it was too heavy.
Desperately he pulled against the weight of the chain to
slip it over the upright fluke. It was almost clear when he
felt the strain increase, and Chris phoned: "That's all
we've got. We're down to the bitter end."

Larry put one foot against the fluke and pulled with all his strength. It was no use, the chain was inexorably drawn from his straining fingers. But he had changed the angle of chain to anchor slightly; and as he watched, the anchor twisted, the chain came off the fluke and the anchor somersaulted. The fluke disappeared as it bit deeply into the mud, the right way, and the anchor took hold.

"Okay," he jubilantly told Chris as he moved to a safe distance from the straining chain.

Shortly after, Chris was able to report that he had the engine running, but would keep it in neutral till the wind dropped, unless they started dragging again. It's not the thing to do for a diver to surface under a boat with a turning propeller.

The whole crisis was over as suddenly as it had arisen. The squall blew itself out; Chris shut off the engine to play safe, and Larry was brought to the surface. He was shaken by the experience, his first real scrape since he had begun diving, but at least, he reassured himself, he had kept his wits about him and had not surrendered to panic.

The next day they spent getting set up for operations. The rented barges were moored on either side of the wreck, while a heavy mushroom anchor was dropped for the *Chinook*. They planned to live aboard until the barge was raised, in order to save time—though the *Chinook* would be crowded with the three Cahill boys and the Miller brothers, Ed and Andy, two old school friends of Chris' whom they had hired to help Peter with topside operations.

Larry went down again to see if the wreck had shifted. Its position seemed unchanged. He moved forward on the barge, about where the tunnel would have to go, and slid down to the bottom. Everything went black as he slid into the mud. He'd have to operate entirely by feel. He worked his way close in under the barge, and felt around beneath the bottom. Just as he had suspected, the mud under the barge, although slightly compressed, was still soft. He adjusted his exhaust, and kicking and twisting himself clear of the clinging mud, floated up to the deck again. He was going to have to drive a tunnel under that barely balanced hulk. And he didn't like the idea. Not one bit.

CHAPTER *10*

~~~~~~

Peter had organized the equipment like a veteran. He had the high-pressure water pumps set up, a big four-stage compressor ready, and two 120 foot lengths of reinforced rubber hose, six inches in diameter, with an air connection at one end. One hose was slung over each side of the sunken barge, and Chris and Larry made the ends fast to the wreck.

Two fire hoses were let down on either side of the hulk, each branch pipe anchored with a heavy weight. The air feeds were coupled to the free ends of the big rubber hoses, to force in air and create a suction that would dredge up lumps of mud as big as a man's head and belch them out of the upper end secured to the top of the barge. Coiled in the mud where Larry had decided to drive the tunnel was ten fathoms of one-inch wire which he would take under the barge to Chris. This would later be used to haul the heavy lifting cables in place.

Chris and Larry sat on the *Chinook's* deck, with helmets, boots and weights removed, and talked things over. Larry's side of the barge was buried about four feet into the mud, while Chris' side was eight or more feet deep. Chris would clear away obstructions on the deck, secure the boom, then make a deep trench. Larry would drive the tunnel through from the seaward side till it met the hole Chris would have ready. Larry would have to travel about twenty-five feet under the wreck.

Larry was fussing with his exhaust valve, which had been letting a trickle of cold water back into the helmet, though he had said nothing to Chris about the leak.

"Take it easy, Larry," said Chris as Peter and one of the Miller boys began helping them to get ready. "Remember to make your walls slope outward. Mud's always dangerous."

"Right," answered Larry. "And you keep your lines clear—and make that hole deep enough!"

Peter laced Larry's boots tightly, so the mud wouldn't pull them off. They rehearsed their signals again; then Peter put on the weights, screwed on the helmet and locked it, and turned on the air.

Peter checked the phones and asked, "Are you sure that valve is okay?"

"Don't worry," said Larry. "It only lets in a few drops. A little uncomfortable after a while, but it's not serious."

Larry stopped at the end of his down line and checked the exact location of the hoses and dredger. Then he dropped into the murk and groped toward them. Feeling along the barge's side, he located the rivet line which was to guide him down and under the steel hull. Without that line, he would lose all sense of direction. Then he called Peter, and told him to get the dredger going.

There was a thunderous rumbling superimposed on the roar of the exhaust valve as the air was forced into the rubber pipe and out toward the surface. Even six feet away the suction was apparent. As the dredge drew up the light surface silt, the water cleared momentarily, then clouded as mud settled from the upper end. They were not attempting to move the dredged mud any great distance. Once it was sucked up and clear of the trench or the tunnel, it was allowed to disperse and settle to the bottom.

Larry's first task was to dig a deep trench running fore and aft alongside the barge. The bottom of an underwater tunnel must start deep and rise gradually toward the far end, so that the diver can keep his exhaust valve higher than the rest of his suit. If it gets lower, the air will rush to the area of least water pressure, which is the highest point, and the diver could be spread-eagled in an inflated dress.

Larry dug a large, slope-sided pit down to the level at which he could safely begin tunneling. With one water hose wedged next to and parallel to the barge's side, to prevent a build-up beneath the barge, he straddled the second hose and called for the jet.

The jet hose writhed suddenly. First came a rush of air bubbles, then a solid jet of water whose back pressure nearly tore the hose from Larry's clutching hands. A jet hose is hard to handle because the nozzle is pushed backward by the force of the water, just as a powerful gun recoils against the shooter's shoulder. This backward thrust can be eased by special compensating holes in the nozzle. Part of the jet stream is thrust backwards through these holes, tending to equalize the force of the jet. The Cahills were operating on too tight a budget to get a special nozzle, but they had drilled several holes which helped counteract the thrust. It was strenuous work, just the same.

Crouched deep in the mud, Larry directed the jet in an arc with a gradually increasing radius, forcing the loosened mud in the direction of the suction dredge which gulped it up. The jet stirred up great clouds of black mud, which combined with the mud spewing forth from the upper end of the suction dredge and then gradually dispersed and settled in the water. It had seemed dark before, but now every vestige of light was cut off.

Staying within arm's length of the wreck's bottom, to keep from losing direction, Larry worked back and forth through clinging, waist-deep mud, battling the jet hose, which seemed like a wild thing, while he gradually widened and deepened the eighteen foot trench. As time went on he had to take frequent rests, lying pillowed in the mud.

When the trench was finished, he surfaced for a light lunch and a break.

Chris had been clearing the decks of the barge, but he expected to be able to start digging his own trench after their midday break and have it finished in good time. He would then start tunneling from his end. After an hour they both descended again.

Larry's dredge line had been left running while he was topside, even though his jet was turned off. He found the bottom of the trench relatively firm. It was deep enough now to start tunneling . . . the wreck's bottom being just above his eye level as he stood in the trench. This was the beginning of the critical phase . . . driving directly under the hulk.

For a few minutes Larry couldn't quite bring himself to start the tunnel, even though he knew the chance of the barge coming down on him was one in a thousand. Perhaps he should make the trench bigger, before starting the tunnel? But that was only a stall, and he knew it. He dragged the mouth of the dredge down to the center of the trench, where it would suck up the mud as he washed it loose. A light line made fast to the spare hose which was to be left at the mouth of the tunnel was knotted for every yard, so he could tell how far he had gone. Then, holding his breath, he told Peter to start the jet.

Larry knelt and forced the jet into the wall of mud. Then, twisting and turning it, he pried loose great chunks and gobs of mud and washed them back to where the dredge could suck them in. At each change of position he would reach up to the rivet line, where the steel plates of the bottom were riveted to a frame inside, to confirm his position. Then he had to lie flat on his stomach across the pulsating hose, forcing the jet ahead of him, and pulling the clods of mud he washed loose back past his body. He could tunnel only for a couple of feet; then he had to stop, back out of the narrow cut, and drag in the hungry dredge to draw out the loose mud which had accumulated.

Each time he backed out for the dredge, he was able to stand up a moment . . . a welcome change, and a necessary one, too, because it permitted the water that had trickled into the helmet through the leaky exhaust valve to drain down into his dress. Lying almost motionless in the tunnel, he was rapidly growing cold, but his knotted line finally told him that he was at mid-point, and he felt a surge of confidence that the ordeal would soon be over.

The crisis, when it came, was not sudden. Only gradually did Larry realize that he was in trouble. Now that he was on the home stretch, he had been using the jet for a longer period than usual. Lying there across the hose, he could feel the mud he had washed loose pushing against his sides. Then he realized that there was pressure against his back as well. That was wrong.

He buzzed Peter to shut off the jet. As the hose went limp, Larry pressed his hands against the mud wall and tried to worm his way back. Nothing happened. His legs were hard to move; the pressure all over was slowly growing excessive; he could feel his helmet being gradually pushed downward. Then there was a groaning sound and a trembling vibration in the barge above him. Slowly the pressure of the mud encasing him increased. The wreck was slipping. It had collapsed the tunnel.

Then Larry panicked. Writhing and struggling, he battled frantically to fight his way out. His heart pounded and he breathed in great gulps, his lungs burning up the oxygen in the air supply.

Such panic cannot last long. A man either becomes a complete lunatic, loses every bit of reason and changes to pure animal, or he calms down a little. Trembling violently, wet with sweat, still panting, Larry finally won the battle for some measure of self-control. The movement of the barge had stopped. There was no further increase in pressure.

He was lying on his right side, but completely immobilized. He and Chris had timed their tunneling so that the most critical period would come at slack tide. Larry had no idea of time, but he guessed the tide must be ebbing now. It would be a good idea to get out of there before the tide was running in full force, because the ebb tide was most likely to start the wreck moving again. The pressure hose was buried somewhere below him. Normally, soft muck, quicksand, or a soft silty bottom hold no terrors for the diver. If he sinks deeply in it, it is merely a case of negative buoyancy, and letting in more air to increase buoyancy will break him out. But Larry couldn't reach his valve, and even if he could inflate his dress, he'd be held down by the bottom of the barge which was so close above him. There was nothing he could do but tell Peter to get Chris down there fast, to wash him out with the spare hose.

Larry lowered his head inside his immovable helmet to rest his aching neck muscles. His chin touched water! Unable to drain down into the diving dress, the trickle of water from the leaky exhaust valve was forming a pool right under his chin. He could feel the cold swirling of it against his cheek as he pressed the buzzer with his chin. It would take a long time for that trickle to fill his dress, but it would in time, and he might be down there a long while. His voice was shaky as he told Peter about it. "The phone mouthpiece will be flooded in a few minutes, but the buzzer and earphone will be clear for a while. I won't be able to talk, but I can hear, and I'll buzz once for 'yes' and twice for 'no.' Tell Chris not to waste any time."

After what seemed an endless wait, Peter's trembling voice sounded in Larry's ear. "How long do you think you can hold out?"

"How should I know?" demanded Larry hysterically. Then, more calmly, "Half an hour, maybe. Is Chris on his way yet?" Larry could visualize his older brother dropping everything and charging to his rescue, and felt a little better. The next, hesitating message from Peter struck him numb.

"Chris tried to come up too fast when I told him you were caught," said Peter. "He fouled his lines somehow, but he says he'll be clear any minute, and to hold on."

"Hold on!" screamed Larry. "What else can I do? I'm helpless. Tell Chris to come. Tell him to come." Suddenly he realized that the water in his helmet was already up to his mouthpiece. "Can you hear me, Peter?" There was no answer. He pressed the buzzer, and Peter came on, asking him if he could do anything. "Can you hear me?" he repeated, but the words did not get through.

For a long period, Larry lay there, his fists clenched, sobbing helplessly. Peter kept talking reassuringly, but Larry had stopped listening. If only he had let Chris drive the tunnel. If only Sam Dougherty had not run out on them. If only he had stayed at school. This was a crazy business, anyway, dragging logs out of Puget Sound. His mother was right. She'd always been afraid something like this would happen. His mother! He began to cry and moan. But this spell ran out, and he recovered a little. He began to count, very slowly . . . but he'd get to the forties and forget whether or not he had skipped the thirties. He prayed. He had been as religious as most boys . . . he knew dozens of prayers by heart . . . but none of them came to him now. He talked directly to the Almighty. He didn't say: "Save me and I'll be a better boy," or "I'll go to church every day." He said only, "Get me out of this, God. God, please get me out of this. Please, Please." He felt a little more calm.

The water was so deep now in his helmet that he had to twist his head to one side to breathe. As his exhausted emotions quieted, he realized that Peter was reiterating over and over the same question to him on the earphone. "Shall I step up the pressure, Larry? Will that help keep out the water?"

Suddenly he felt a twinge of pity for Peter. In his inexperience, Peter wouldn't know what was the correct thing to do. He must be in an agony of indecision. Thinking of Peter instead of himself did more than anything yet to restore Larry to rational thought. Greater pressure might help hold back the water. But it would also inflate the diving dress . . . make it harder for Chris to wash him free. Not an easy decision. He buzzed twice. No. Maybe as a last resort, but not now.

Peter came on again. "Larry! Chris has surfaced! He'll be down in a minute."

Time dragged on. Larry's head and shoulders ached so intolerably with the effort of holding his mouth clear that he would let his face hang in the water every few minutes, then raise it again to breathe. There was a loud clicking in the earphones. They were changing the plugs.

Chris' strong, steady voice filled the prison of his helmet, "I'm coming, Larry. Don't give up." Good old Chris. No time wasted on words. Chris would have him out.

But nothing seemed to be happening. Then, suddenly, came a blow on the lead soles of his boots, followed by a battering and buffeting as the ninety pound pressure jet played around his legs, his torso, his shoulders. The jet hit his helmet, and there was a spout of water from that infernal exhaust valve. The jet stopped. Larry felt Chris hitch his air and life lines around his ankles. He pushed against the mud with his imprisoned hands, and moved back an inch. Slowly he slid out of the new tunnel Chris had dug.

Larry didn't even realize he had reached the trench till he felt Chris freeing his lines. Chris helped him to his feet, and as Larry clung to him, the water in his helmet poured down inside his dress until it was up to his chest. Larry was only partly conscious as Chris put the down line in his hand. Chris inflated his own dress to the danger point to provide extra buoyancy for Larry's flooded rig.

As Larry struggled up the ladder on the *Chinook*, with Peter and the Miller boys hauling him from above, the water inside his dress dropped to waist level. Andy Miller held his shoulders, and Peter removed his helmet. Larry looked dazed. He tried to smile, but his jaw muscles twitched. He walked unsteadily across the deck to the shelter cabin, where he lay down on a berth. Peter swathed him in blankets.

Chris kept the others quiet, while Peter heated some soup. After Larry had downed it, he felt a little stronger. Then he talked. He had a moment or two of near-hysteria, but conquered it. Gradually his nerves quieted; his narrative slowed; and then in mid-sentence he was asleep.

CHAPTER *11*

~~~~~~

There was a strange constraint among the brothers next day, when it came time to resume operations. Oddly enough, Chris was readier to quit than Larry. But Peter resolved the matter by the way he put it. "If the job's too much for us, maybe we should hire some outside divers." Neither Chris nor Larry was prepared to admit defeat to that extent.

"It was one of those odd combinations of bad breaks," admitted Chris. "There wasn't a chance in a hundred that the barge would slip just then; and not a chance in a hundred that I'd pick that same moment to get fouled up. But both had to happen at once."

"The worst of it is," said Larry, "the barge is still down there. We still haven't gotten a tunnel under it, and it's one day less before the extension on our loan runs out. Talking won't raise that barge."

So they went down again. Chris wanted to drive the tunnel, but they compromised by taking turns. The hole Chris had driven to rescue Larry was still open, and this time the operation went exactly as it should.

With everything clicking, they got the cables under the barge, the pontoons in place, and sealed all of the deck openings in the hull. Air was pumped through hoses into the hull and into the four pontoons, forcing out the water with which they were filled. It was a tricky business, because any inequalities in lift could capsize the barge and set them back in worse shape than when they started. The deeply embedded barge was held not only by its weight, but also by the suction underneath it. Jets were used again to try to break the suction by getting water between the bottom of the barge and the muck. Neither Chris nor Larry cared to do much more tunneling.

The time came for the raising. Their breaths held to the point of pain, they waited and watched the bursting bubbles, the froth of mud, and then . . . the barge broke the surface and floated with its deck barely awash.

But what a mess! It looked as if it would take a month just to scrape off the scum and slime. They had just twelve days to fulfill their contract.

Standing knee deep in the muck, they went to work, trying to reassure one another that it wasn't so bad. They started at the bow and worked aft, elbow deep in mud, taking time out only occasionally to grin at one another's horrible appearance. First they used shovels; then power hoses; then rags, brooms, scrapers. They didn't work any special hours—they worked them all, night and day.

They were all exhausted, Peter especially. Chris tried to get Peter to break off, but he would not. Despite all his hard topside work, he never completely lost the feeling that Chris and Larry were carrying a bigger share of the burden than he. In this filthy job of cleaning the barge and restoring its equipment, Peter actually did more work than any one of them, in spite of his lack of robustness. The strain was telling . . . Peter was drawing on his last reserves.

Events were timed for a Hollywood climax. There was barely time after the crane barge was clean and in operation to get a load of logs up and make their deadline. Chris and Larry got ready to go down.

They had figured that about twenty-eight logs would make up their load. There wouldn't be time for more, anyway. Each diver thus had to attach seven cables, two logs to a line. Larry passed up the first few he located. Two were rotten with teredos, three more were puny. Then he hit a batch of beauties, all of them over three feet across and solid as a rock. Peter called down through the phone: "How you doing, Pappy?"

"Fine. Swell. How about you and the clock?" answered Larry.

"Get going—time's a-wasting."

In a little over an hour, Larry had six cables attached, with one more to go. Peter told him that Chris had finished and was surfacing. Larry was whistling to himself in his helmet, feeling that at last they were over the hump. A five-foot sand shark swam up to give him the once over. He slapped it on the snout and told it to find another playmate—he was busy.

There was his last log—a whopper that must have measured close to four feet across. It was one of a heap of logs. As Larry moved toward it, he saw a pile of empty shells and other debris, and, looking closely, the snake-like arm of an octopus.

Larry had seen plenty of octopuses—they were an old story. Most were small, and they had scuttled back to their hiding places. But Larry wanted that last log, octopus or no octopus. The devil-fish would undoubtedly have preferred to keep away from Larry, but when Larry twisted the cable around the beam of the log—disturbing the octopus' very nest, it decided that was too much. It swarmed over the diver.

Larry wasn't much alarmed. Peter called him, "What's the matter, Larry? What's tugging on your line?"

"Octopus," said Larry.

"Come on up," ordered Peter, who had heard Chris and Larry talk of seeing octopuses, but had never encountered one himself.

"In a minute," said Larry. "This is my last log. Okay. Now haul me up, and get set on deck. I'm bringing company."

The octopus was not a particularly big one. Larry was in no special danger, and knew it. But when Peter saw Larry with the ugly creature clinging to him like a monstrous spider sprawled over its victim, he grabbed an axe and attacked it so savagely that Chris had to take the axe from him by force, lest he injure Larry too.

They all laughed at the incident, but Peter's laughter was weak. Peter looked sick, and Chris ordered him below to his bunk. They got the logs aboard, and headed for the Imperial Pulp and Paper docks. Mr. Norton saw them from his office window, and came out to greet them. It was a great moment—everyone jubilant—triumphant—except Peter. Peter was really sick.

CHAPTER *12*

~~~~~~

　　With equipment restored, Chris and Larry were able to deliver several loads to Imperial Pulp and Paper. Initially, they selected the most favorable locations, where they knew the choicest logs were to be found close together, and where the haul to the company docks was shortest. They were skimming the cream. Operations gradually became slower as they began to work the bottom more intensively, and to move farther from their base.

　　They were all concerned about Peter, who was not responding to medical treatment as rapidly as he should. Larry therefore was rebellious when Chris began proposing more and more insistently that he return to the Sparling School and complete his training in advanced underwater techniques.

　　"Work will slow down to a crawl if I go," he protested. "With Peter laid up and me in school, only one diver on the bottom and the Miller boys, who are still pretty green, on top, you aren't going to bring in much money."

"Let's not get greedy," was Chris' reply. "We've been spoiled by these first big loads. I knew it wouldn't be that easy for long. There's a decent living for us for some years in the Bay and in nearby parts of the Sound. You'll only be away a month, and we have enough money to get along. I want you to be something more than an underwater wood-picker."

"I'm satisfied for now," said Larry. "Why don't we wait till Peter's better, anyway?"

"I'm trying to act like a sensible businessman, and look ahead," Chris explained patiently. "Suppose Peter doesn't get well here? Suppose the doctor says we have to send him to a warmer climate? What should we do then?"

"This family'll stick together, whatever happens," said Larry. "If Peter has to go South, we'll all go. But I'll bet he'll get better right here. You wait and see!"

"I'm not making this up, Larry. The doctor *does* say that Peter should live in a warmer, sunnier climate for a year at least."

"Will he be all right then?" Larry asked anxiously.

"The doctor thinks so."

"How does Peter feel about it?"

"He doesn't want to leave the family, and go away alone. On the other hand, he doesn't want to cause us to break up our business just when we've got it going. He's all mixed up in his mind about it, and that's not doing his health any good, either. That's why I think you should go back to the diving school, Larry."

"I don't see what the diving school has to do with it. We'll need money, lots of it, if the whole family moves, and that's what I think we should do. I'll be able to help earn some more money here; down in Wilmington I'll only be an expense."

"Larry, if we're all going to move, our underwater

lumberjacking will be over. We can keep on diving. We
may even be able to have our own company and work for
ourselves instead of for wages. But who knows what kind
of diving we'll be doing? That's why you've got to learn
as much as possible." Chris paused a moment, then said,
"I'll tell you a secret, Larry. I've been tempted to go
down to the Sparling School myself and take a refresher
course. That's impossible now, and anyway, I can learn
some of the new angles on this business from you after
you've finished."

The idea that he could ever teach his idolized older
brother anything struck Larry as ludicrous, but he could
see the force of Chris' reasoning. He would go.

Another family conference was held that night. Always close-knit, the Cahills had become even more closely
tied to one another during their joint logging enterprise.
There was no question of letting Peter go off by himself.
They would sell out, and they'd all go together. There
weren't even many regrets. They hadn't been licked by
the job. They'd proved they could do it. And they even
had some small capital.

The big problem was, where should they go to find
a place suitable for Peter's recovery, that would at the
same time offer a chance for Chris and Larry to use their
diving skills? They reviewed the opportunities. There
were many for unattached men. Calls for divers were
coming from all parts of the world, and a diver who
wanted to see the odd corners of the globe would have no
difficulty doing so on an expense account. Living conditions under these circumstances are not ideal. Divers on
extended operations usually live on ships, boats and barges
which offer few comforts. However, in addition to good
earnings, the profession offers to the man who wants it
freedom from ordinary workday routine, and satisfies the
masculine quest for adventure and the unusual. Never

before in history had divers been so much in demand as in the early Post-War years, or paid so highly.

Lloyds of London has a record of all sunken ships lying in 100 fathoms or less—that is, theoretically practicable for salvage. There are well over a thousand of them sunk as a result of the past war, as well as those lost through war and natural hazards for ages back. Bridge construction and maintenance; underwater pipe lines; demolition; recovery of lost articles; police work, including recovery of bodies, murder weapons, narcotics, and other evidence; building and inspecting dams; sponge and abalone fishing; harvesting agar; ship repair to avoid drydocking; recovering of sunken treasure—these are some of the tasks which insure the diver against unemployment. Many divers work for large companies, but theirs is a trade which permits a man to go into business for himself if he desires, from "mining" gold at the mouths of Alaskan streams to gathering agar—a deep-sea alfalfa which has many uses and brings as much as $85 a ton. In good weather, a diver can gather a ton a day, though it's not all profit, since he must maintain a boat and crew.

Even on wages, a diver does very well indeed, though of course pay varies according to locality. Rates range from $30 per day for a diver without equipment working in shallow water, to $200 to $300 per day for a diver using his own equipment and working in deep water. As in other highly paid professions, the best trained and most experienced men get the most money and the best jobs. Lt. Cross of the Sparling School has received as much at $625 per day for placing 2¾ tons of demolition explosive in a wreck in five days. On another job, involving a dive of 240 feet in icy water into a jagged plane wreck, he received $460 per day with all equipment, tender and expenses paid as well. Yet another time, he was paid $4,100 for thirteen days of particularly deep and hazardous diving. But not many divers can match the skill and experience of Cross. Certainly the Cahill boys could not. A more usual rate is $105 per day for diver, tender and equipment, with special equipment or skills adding to the amount paid.

There are three broad fields of deep sea diving: military, commercial, and open sea. Military divers will be found wherever the armed services have work to be done, whether recovering an anchor at Wake Island or a sunken liner in Tokyo. While they occasionally hire commercial divers, most of the armed forces' peacetime work is done by their own men. The commercial diver is expected to be able to perform almost any underwater job. He uses explosives to blast for hardpan or to remove obstructions; he must be able to weld and burn under water; must be a rigger and a caulker, a plumber, a mason, and a carpenter. All these jobs are much tougher than when done above water. Poor visibility is only one of the difficulties. In submarine blasting, for example, the work to be performed by the explosive is increased because the pressure is much greater on all sides than in the open air. This necessitates deeper subdrilling, closer spacing, and higher loading factors.

The open sea diver generally is not so skilled a mechanic as the commercial diver. He must know how to combat strong currents and surge. Primarily his objective is to reach the bottom, locate the object of his search, and harvest as much as he can before he must ascend. Most familiar of the open sea category are the Florida sponge divers, abalone, agar, moss and shell divers. They are usually paid on a piece or ton basis. New fields such as offshore oil well drillings and submarine gold mining offer many opportunities, especially to divers with engineering backgrounds. The submerged coastal shelf of the United States holds our greatest untapped oil reserve, calculated at ten billion barrels, or one-third of the present known reserve.

The Cahills reviewed all of these possibilities, and finally settled on Florida. The climate would be ideal for Peter; there was sponge fishing, though that was a hard field for strangers to break into; there were many torpedoed ships in the Gulf and West Indies region. There were, as Larry pointed out with sparkling eyes, more sunken treasure ships in that area than anywhere else on earth. And Chris was acquainted with the area from his Coast Guard service.

"You didn't happen to run into any treasure ships when you were in the Caribbean, did you, Chris?" asked Larry.

"Not even one," laughed Chris.

"No pirate maps, even? No mysterious sunken hulks you stumbled on?" Larry was joking, but Chris had a surprise for him.

"I did find one wreck that nobody else in Puerto Rico seemed to know existed," said Chris. "Ran across it when we were helping the Air Force recover some practice torpedoes."

"Honestly?" demanded Larry. "You're not making this up?"

"No," said Chris. "I really did find one. The skipper marked it on his chart, and we tried to find some record of it back in San Juan, but there didn't seem to be any. In the Mona Passage, it was; between Mona Isle and Hispaniola."

"Hispaniola!" Larry yelped. "That was the name of Jim Hawkins' ship, in *Treasure Island!*" He was really excited now.

"Don't blow your top, Larry," Chris laughed. "This was no Spanish galleon. The water is deep there, and all I saw was the truck of her mast and an outline of her shape.

But she was a steamer—a small one and not very modern, from the look of her rigging. I doubt she had been down there over fifty years."

"Fifty years," Larry reflected. "That would be around the time of the Spanish-American War. She could have been sunk then, while she was trying to escape from the American Fleet."

"Maybe," agreed Chris. "Still, you'd think there'd be a record in San Juan. Puerto Rico was Spanish then. Anyway, you can get any ideas of treasure hunting out of your head, young man. More money is spent trying to recover treasure than all the treasure that's found is worth. And we're not going to be grubbing around in the holds of a lot of unidentified wrecks that would have been salvaged before now, if salvage were possible at all and if they had anything in them worth the trouble. Whatever we work on in Florida, it won't be sunken treasure. Forget it, Larry. Put it out of your mind."

If there's one word that's almost impossible to put out of the mind of an adventurous young man, it's treasure. Larry knew it was childish, but the word stuck, and it brought some wonderful dreams on his long trip back to finish his training at the Sparling School of Deep Sea Diving.

CHAPTER *13*

The transition from the Puget Sound country, which lies about as far to the northwest as you can go in the United States, to the Florida Keys, which is as far to the southeast as you can go, was an exciting but not entirely comfortable experience for the Cahill family.

The Cahills wanted to locate at least semi-permanent quarters. With the Florida resort season just starting, housing was impossible to find except at prohibitive rates —even at this distance from the main resorts. They stayed temporarily in a motel, but were uncomfortable among the people they met.

The turning point came unexpectedly, rising out of an incident at a nearby restaurant to which the Cahills had gone one sultry evening. There was a bar at the entrance—a feature which did not recommend the place to Mrs. Cahill, but it was the only inexpensive restaurant near their lodgings. She was encouraged, too, when an elderly but vigorous gentleman accompanied by two girls, apparently his daughters, took a table near them. He was a handsome man, wearing casual clothes with an air that gave them distinction. One look at the girls made all three Cahill boys sit up straighter in their chairs, smooth back their hair, and become very careful of their table manners.

A noisy group of young men in the bar began by their antics to disturb the diners across the hallway. With a start Larry recognized Max Gsovski among them. He looked Larry straight in the eye, without a glimmering of recognition. Larry was satisfied. He would have felt embarrassed and ashamed if Max had spoken to him in the presence of those two pretty girls.

The group in the bar were making a great show of being tough. They were not unaware of the two girls in the dining room, and were obviously trying to impress them. The remarks began to become louder and rougher and aimed more directly at the girls. Their father flushed, pushed back his chair, and started to rise. The Cahill boys were up first.

"Perhaps it would be better if we handled this," said Chris respectfully. Chris was completely calm. He seldom had to endure physical attack or even threats. Looking at Chris' bulging muscles, heavy chest and shoulders, and determined chin, most men were content to thank heaven for having made him good-natured.

The boys entered the bar, and Chris turned on the four men. "You're going to cut this out right now—with no more conversation."

The proprietor, who had been cowed by the four toughs, now plucked up courage when the Cahills intervened, and advanced with a rolling pin in his fat fist. He didn't look particularly formidable, but the crew of cooks and dishwashers he had mustered in the kitchen did. "I called the police on you," he shouted excitedly. "You better get out fast." They did—not quietly, not without threats, but not slowly either. The proprietor took Chris' hand in his warm, moist one, and said, "No check at your table, young man. Eat anything you want. It's on the house!"

The elderly gentleman also advanced to express his approval and gratitude, and that of his daughters. So it was in this story-book fashion, that the Cahills first met Sēnor Nemesio Currier and his daughters Mona and Linda.

Mr. Currier and his daughters lived on a boat. Not a shanty-boat but a 30,000-dollar 45-foot sport cruiser, *La Princessa*, moored in a slip leading off to the Gulf. There was no hardship involved in this type of existence. Besides her own power plant, *La Princessa* had shore-side electricity, water, bottled gas, even a telephone. She was a lovely thing, with satiny topsides, teak decks, glistening bright work and polished chromium. Under her hatches were two spic and span 160 horsepower marine engines that could push her along at eighteen knots without a tremor.

Mr. Currier proposed that the Cahills try to find a suitable boat, and join the considerable population of Florida who had broken ties with real estate and did their living afloat. Through Mr. Currier, the Cahills were introduced to several members of this unconventional group, and found them delightful. There was an easy, unforced camaraderie among the people who lived in the boats that took no account of money or social standing or even native intelligence. The alchemy that wrought this miracle was the peculiar world of boats, and their love for them.

Joining this group seemed an ideal solution to the Cahills' problems. Furthermore, searching for a boat is a pleasant pastime. Peter and Larry had already fallen victims to the easy life and gentle climate. Peter's health was mending rapidly, but he and Larry had passed from a world of activity to a world of dreams and loafing.

Chris alone had retained his energy and determination. His hope now was to find a boat in which the Cahills could live, yet which would also be usable for shallow water diving. This was a tall order, for a good diving boat has certain features not easy to find.

In this respect, Mr. Currier was a tremendous help. He knew every boatyard on the Coast, and a high proportion of the available craft. Chris was scrupulous in accepting the advice and recommendations of Mr. Currier, because he recognized the man's great knowledge of the subject, and his astonishingly exact appreciation of the qualities necessary in a boat to be used by a diver.

After a week of futile search, Mr. Currier received a letter from a friend in Fort Lauderdale, describing a boat that seemed ideal. Chris hired a station wagon, and the Cahills and Curriers drove up together to examine it. The boat fit their specifications perfectly. It was a Chesapeake Bay "bugeye," a shoal draft schooner at least fifty years old, but apparently still sound. Her history made her even more desirable. She was named the *Hannah P. Pettingale*, a name which amused Mrs. Cahill and shocked Larry, who immediately began to think up more appropriate names. The *Pettingale* had been built as an oyster boat, but had been later purchased and used by the Maryland police to catch oyster pirates—proof that she was fast and able. She looked piratical herself, with her bold sheer, clipper bow, sharp stern, and two tall raking masts. About sixty feet over-all, she had ample beam—seventeen feet—for stability; low topsides, which would make it easy to rig diving ladders and stages; heavy scantlings which would support the weight of a compressor and other heavy equipment needed for diving; broad uncluttered decks for the many activities of the divers and topside men. She still had one of her cargo holds, providing ample storage room; and the extreme rake of her masts which gave her the look of a privateer would make it easy to rig booms for hoisting heavy weights.

While Chris was examining the *Pettingale's* qualifications as a practical diving boat, Mrs. Cahill and the Currier girls were studying the living accommodations. They were not quite so ideal. There was a small cuddy aft, with a chart table and two narrow berths, a main saloon with dining table and settees, four small cabins, a galley and a head. As far as space went, it was adequate, but it was rough and dirty, and littered with odds and ends of equipment, tools and the refuse of ships' carpentry. However, Mrs. Cahill was just the person to conquer a mess of that kind.

The *Pettingale* was owned by a syndicate of four men who had planned to sail her around the world. They had moved her to Florida, rebuilt her heavy hull, sheathed her bottom with copper, but had run out of money before they could complete refitting of her sails, rigging, or auxiliary engine. The four men were now bickering among themselves and the *Pettingale* was put up for sale.

Chris would have bought her on the spot in a burst of unusual enthusiasm, but Mr. Currier insisted on a professional survey. "A boat as old as this is liable to have dry rot in her somewhere, and dry rot is like cancer. That copper sheathing on her bottom is fine for tropical water, but we'd better have some of it off to be sure the teredos haven't been in her before they put it on."

"We know about the teredos, don't we, Chris," remarked Larry, thinking of their Port Hemlock experience.

The marine surveyor gave his grudging approval of the hull, though he was frankly scornful of the spars and rigging.

"Masts might stay up if you renew all the standing

rigging," he grumbled, "but them spars and sails and running rigging is worthless. Better check the sheaves in all the blocks, too."

The price was not low. "They say money isn't worth as much nowadays," Chris remarked ruefully, "but it doesn't seem to have gone altogether out of style around here." But she was so ideally suited to their requirements that Chris, after some long bargaining and a slight concession on the price, finally nodded his head. "We'll take her."

"You've got a real boat, Chris," Mr. Currier told him. Larry was almost jumping with delight. "When can we move aboard?" he demanded.

"I'd suggest you bring her down to Key Largo and fit out there," said Mr. Currier. "You can berth near me, and I know just the man to help you on the rigging. It'll cost a lot less than having the work done in a shipyard."

"When can we bring her down?" Larry wanted to know.

Chris looked doubtfully at the rusty shrouds and stays, and the dirty gray canvas of her sails. "Think we could move her the way she is now?" he asked Mr. Currier.

"I think so, if the engine will run, and you pick your weather. Matter of fact, this would have been a good day —the wind's fair. If you want to stay here and come down tomorrow, I'll drive Mrs. Cahill back to Key Largo and return the car."

"What do you say, Mother?" asked Chris.

"I'm agreeable," Mrs. Cahill answered. "Only I'm going along on the maiden voyage, if Mr. Currier will return the car."

So it was arranged.

CHAPTER *14*

Getting the *Hannah P. Pettingale* ready to sail proved anything but easy. In their enthusiasm for her good qualities, the brothers had unconsciously minimized the deplorable state of all elements of motive power, alow and aloft. While Mrs. Cahill was trying to bring enough order out of the chaos below for them to sleep aboard that night, Chris tackled the greasy giant that filled the engine room. Larry and Peter tried to make sense of her running and standing rigging.

The principal handicap for Larry and Peter was ignorance. They were both experts at handling power boats; they knew something of marine engines and what made them tick; but their experience in sailing craft was limited to the small sloops they had fooled around with on Puget Sound. The maze of heavy rigging on the *Pettingale* dismayed them both.

There was no chance of getting away the next day; too many essential tasks were uncompleted. This proved fortunate, for Mr. Currier arrived in the morning to see them leave, and decided to stay over and make the trip with them. His encyclopedic knowledge of sailing and rigging was to prove a godsend.

By the following morning, Chris had the engine running at a fairly respectable cadence, though it would still give an occasional hop and skip when he opened the throttle. They decided to cast off. Their departure was quiet and uneventful, except when they parted a stern line, tore off a fender, uprooted a few feet of rubstrake, and narrowly missed ramming a spanking new yacht which only a Texas billionaire could afford. All because of a stalled engine at the most critical moment. It seemed an ill omen for the trip, but things went smoothly for the first few hours.

As the *Pettingale* moved majestically through a drawbridge while dozens of motorists gaped or impatiently honked, the bridge tender favored them with a sour glance. "H-A-N-N-A-H P. P-E-T-T-I-N-G-A-L-E" he painstakingly spelled out in a loud and disapproving voice. "Holy Cow, what a name for a boat!" He stared accusingly at Larry, who was stationed at the ship's wheel and, until then, feeling like John Paul Jones.

This name business had to be settled. "Chris, how about *Jolly Roger?*" Larry demanded.

"Who's he?" Mrs. Cahill wanted to know.

" 'Jolly Roger' was what the buccaneers used to call their flag—the skull and crossbones," Peter explained.

"The name sounds innocent enough, but let's leave out the skeletons," said Mrs. Cahill.

"Larry's still daydreaming about the pirate treasure," said Chris. "But I don't mind the name if Mother and Peter agree."

"It's appropriate enough for this area," volunteered Mr. Currier. "Don't be so cynical about treasure ships, Chris. These are the real treasure waters, off the Keys, in

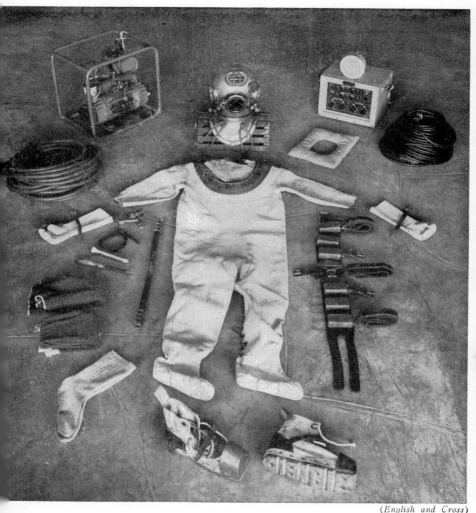

Complete deep sea diving dress. From top clockwise: helmet, helmet cushion, diver's telephone, combination life line and telephone cable (coiled), diver's glove with wrist strap, weighted belt with harness, heavy lead shoes, woolen socks, woolen underwear, knife and case, glove. To right of glove is air control valve. Beside diving dress is 3 ft. whip to connect control valve to helmet; above glove is air hose and air compressor. In center, diving dress.

A log raft being towed down-river into a harbor.

The Chinook, *a typical heavy duty power boat of the Puget Sound area.*

Chris going down to inspect the sunken barge, as Sam tends the lines.

(English and Cross)

ry hits the bottom on his first
e.

(English and Cross)

Lieut. E. R. Cross of the Sparling School of Deep Sea Diving.

Lieut. Cross inspecting and instructing students before their first (elimination) dive.

The Sparling School's training tank. An instructor checks the students' performances and grades them.

Larry leans into the current as he searches for the wrecked diving barge.

Working in heavy kelp, Larry adjusts his air valves.

The Wrangler, *a converted crash boat.*

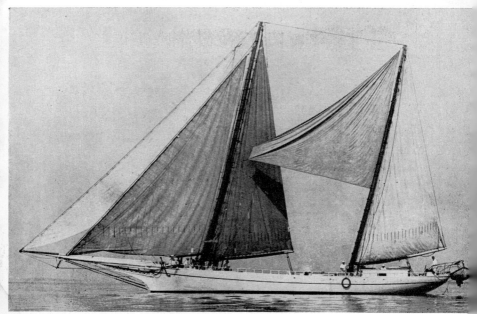

The Jolly Roger *under full sail. The heavy construction, shoal draft an*
stability of this bugeye make her ideal for diving.

Larry "blows-up" at
Mona Island.

(English and Cross)

Larry, about to submerge
with a hammer, adjusts his
air intake.

(English and Cross)

(Hamilton W

The "treasure cave" on Mona Island.

the Bahamas and the West Indies." It was apparent that this was a subject close to Mr. Currier's heart, and he expanded on it at length while the others hung on his words.

It was not a new thought to any of them, for of all ventures by deep sea divers, the search for treasure is most dramatic. In sheer economics, there is a surer fortune to be earned in salvage and repair and construction work, but the lure of tarnished doubloons, moidores and pieces of eight has an appeal not to be counted in dollars and cents.

What's more, Mr. Currier told them, the treasures are truly there. You can read about them, even get approximate locations, in a dozen books. Down at Venanguebe Bay, just off Ngoncy Island, is a French frigate that went down in 1781 with treasure aboard. The galleon *Florencia* still lies in Tobermory Bay in Scotland, with millions in waiting treasure. Or you could try the Auckland Islands, far south in the Pacific, where the sailing ship *General Grant*, bound from Australia to London, was lost with 50,000 ounces of gold. In Jamaica there lies the sunken pirate city of Port Royal; the waters of the Bahamas and the West Indies hold scores of Spanish plate ships in their grasp. In the vicinity of Key Largo, not far from where *La Princessa* lay, a whole treasure flotilla of fourteen great galleons was wrecked on uncharted reefs during a sudden storm. Tens of millions lie somewhere strewn over the coral—and not in deep water, either. Sir William Phipps won riches, knighthood, and eventually governorship of a province with a small part of the treasure of Silver Shoals. The *Hussar*, with more than $2,500,000 in gold that was to have been paid to British soldiers in the Revolution, lies about one hundred yards off Randall's Island in New York's East River. His Britannic Majesty's man-of-war *Lutine*, with a cargo of gold and silver bars and coin, has lain since 1799 between the islands of Vlieland and Terschelling, off the coast of Holland.

Great wealth still lies in the harbor of Vigo, Spain, as a result of an attack by a British fleet in 1702 on seventeen treasure ships laden with gold and silver in coins and great ingots. Due to the War of the Spanish Succession, this treasure had been allowed to accumulate in Porto Bello and Cartagena during three years. According to Mr. Currier, modern estimates set the value at $150,000,000. Thirteen galleons went to the bottom. A good deal of gold and silver has been recovered, but even more remains in the clutches of the sea. Jules Verne, in his *Twenty Thousand Leagues Under the Sea,* describes an imaginary salvage of the gold of Vigo Bay by his hero, Captain Nemo. Most of the precious metal is still there.

In 1798, a British sloop of war, the *Braak* was caught in a sudden squall in Old Kiln Roads, off Cape Henlopen, Delaware. There happened one of those sudden tragedies that darkened the days of sail. The *Braak* capsized and sank in ninety feet of water, carrying with her a fortune in gold captured from five rich galleons— estimated at ten million dollars.

A more recent treasure lies in the SS *Merida,* sunk in a collision in 1911 off Cape Charles, Va. The *Merida* carried in her purser's safes bullion, specie and jewels worth almost five million dollars belonging to the Mexican tyrant Porfirio Diaz, who was fleeing from the revolutionary forces of Madero. The *Merida* was actually located in two hundred feet of water by a Danish diver named Fred Nielsen, who identified her positively. The discovery was followed by a terrific storm, which must have shifted the wreck, and it has never been found again.

The list went on and on, for Mr. Currier was dealing with his life's enthusiasm. "There's the torpedoed British vessel *Elizabethville*," he told them, "with a cargo of diamonds waiting off the coast of Africa. And the *Oslander*, which was sunk by an iceberg off Taku Inlet in Alaska, with five million in Klondike gold."

Fort Knox, he told them, is a small boy's piggy bank compared to Davy Jones' hoard. Experts say that there are 260 billion dollars in treasure strewn along the coasts of the North and South American continents.

He told them how, in 1951, an alert yachtsman spotted ancient, coral encrusted cannon in shallow water off the coast of Florida. Underwater inspection disclosed the remains of three vessels, estimated to have come to grief in the seventeenth and eighteenth centuries. You can imagine what happened next. Many relics, including the ancient cannon, have been recovered. "Treasure?" Mr. Currier blinked. "*Quién sabe?*"

He related how, in the early spring of 1949, William Cottrell, a retired fisherman, picked up a golden doubloon on the beach at Highlands, N.J. More coins were found —a total of twenty-four, probably tossed on the beach in a dredging operation, or swept from a disintegrating wreck. Not long ago an American sailor discovered a skeleton half buried on the beach of Grand Canyon in the Bahamas, with a dagger in its back. Nearby natives for years have been picking up occasional gold pieces on this stretch of sand. "There must be a treasure ship somewhere off this beach," said Mr. Currier. "How'd you like to go look for it?"

Chris, who was the only one of the Cahills not completely enchanted by this discourse, laughed. "I've heard rumors about an American deep sea diver who has his own private galleon. Rather than salvage the complete treasure and lose nearly all of it in confiscatory taxes, he brings up only enough gold each year for his needs, which, however, are not modest."

Mr. Currier nodded sagely. "It's perfectly possible. And many new treasures have been added to the list during the past war. The U.S. Army dumped 8½ million dollars in silver coin into the sea off Corregidor, to keep it from the Japanese. Some has been salvaged, but a fortune still lies on the bottom. A Central European government threw several million dollars into the Black Sea to keep it from the greedy clutches of the Nazis. At last reports it is still there. What are we waiting for?"

Chris smiled. "I'm waiting for a chance to make an honest living. If any treasure comes my way, I'll be perfectly happy to pick it up. But I know better than to go looking for it."

Mr. Currier regarded Chris steadily. "I'll tell you something no one knows but Mona and Linda. I know where there's a wrecked frigate. It's not a matter of phony maps or deathbed secrets told by supposed survivors. I've stood inside her, and I've recovered quite a few relics from her."

Larry was so engrossed he almost ran the *Jolly Roger* into a passing boat. Even Chris lost his cynicism.

"You really mean it?" he demanded.

"It's absolutely true," said Mr. Currier. "Of course, there's no treasure—." Four hearts fell with a thump. Mr. Currier looked embarrassed.

"I didn't mean to lead you on and then disillusion you," he said. "There may once have been treasure in the wreck, but if there was, it was recovered by someone— probably survivors of the wreck. We were out fishing, the girls and I, trolling for mutton snappers. Mona was at the wheel, and Linda and I were fishing. I was watching the bright-colored little fish swimming among the sea ferns and the clumps of lettuce coral when the reef ended and the bottom fell away. As my eyes got adjusted to the greater depths, I suddenly saw what looked like huge logs, about five or six fathoms down, all crusted with coral and waving sea fern. They were scattered roughly in two rows, and I counted forty of them. I knew they were ancient ship's cannon!"

Mr. Currier's eyes were bright as he savored again the thrill of that magic moment. "What puzzled me at first," he continued, "was that I'd fished that same reef many times—it was a favorite place of mine, because not many boats go there, and sometimes I like to be alone. I knew I'd been in the same spot before, and that those cannon weren't visible. You know how coral is—all curved and convoluted. The straight lines of those cannon couldn't be missed. Then I remembered that we'd had a terrible storm from the southeast since the last time I had fished that reef. The seas must have roiled up the sand, and bottom currents carried it away. The cannon were there all the time. That's why I'm so sure that, if there ever was any treasure, it was recovered around the time of the wreck.

"Well, the girls and I were fairly bursting with our secret, but we've managed to keep it. We all took up skin diving. At first we just looked for gold bar or coins, but when we became sure that there wasn't a real treasure, we started collecting other souvenirs and got a good price for them. I have some of them on the *Princessa*, including a couple of swords, some buttons, and a few coins—one of them an onza—you know, those funny looking eight-sided Spanish coins. I'll show them to you. What I'd like to do now is to raise some of the cannon."

Larry let out his breath. "Gosh, what a wonderful break to find it, even if there wasn't any treasure," he said.

"It's not so surprising," said Mr. Currier. "You know that the records of the Hydographic Office show that the average annual loss of vessels in world commerce is over two thousand. That means about a million ships lost since the year 1500. Remember, these waters around the Keys, the Bahamas and the West Indies are dangerous even now, with accurate charts and modern navigational aids. A big freighter ran aground in the Keys just two months ago. Imagine the risk for ships back in the sixteenth and seventeenth centuries, with charts that were mostly guess-work, unwieldy ships, yes, and pirates. Pirates were a grim reality, and that *Jolly Roger* you've named your boat for was flown in these very waters in anything but a spirit of fun."

Chris was interested in spite of his better judgment. One confidence begets others, and he found himself telling Mr. Currier about the wrecked steamer he had accidentally found while he was stationed in Puerto Rico with the Coast Guard. Mr. Currier was tremendously interested.

"My mother was Puerto Rican," he told them, "and I grew up on a sugar central on the island. You say the wreck was in the Mona Passage, between Mona Island and Hispaniola? That's pretty deep water there."

"Yes, it is," agreed Chris. "But the ship isn't beyond normal deep diving depth. I saw the truck of her mast, and the general outline of her hull and superstructure. She looked kind of old-fashioned, but she was a steamer. I was recovering practice torpedos, and I couldn't explore her. The skipper and I tried to find out something about her, but no one in Puerto Rico had ever heard of a wreck in that spot. It's quite close to Mona Island."

"I know Mona Island well," said Mr. Currier. "I visited it many times as a boy. My family's sugar central was not far from Mayaguez. I named my oldest daughter

'Mona,' after the island, because I had so many happy memories of it, barren though it is. That's where I really began my interest in treasure seeking. I don't know how many days I've spent on Mona Island looking for treasure. I suppose you know that the pirate, William Jennings, buried the loot from scores of Spanish ships on Mona Island? Some of it is believed to have been raised by an expedition in 1939. Why, Puerto Rico was attacked many times by pirates in the old days. St. Thomas, which was the major pirate rendezvous, is only a few miles from Puerto Rico. Captain Kidd sailed from St. Thomas on his last voyage North, just before he was taken and hanged. But getting back to the present, I have lots of connections in Puerto Rico and Havana and the Dominican Republic. Suppose I try to identify the ship? You can't give me a more accurate description, or even guess how old she might be?"

"As best I can remember, she was about 1500 tons; not very big. The angle of her funnel, and the lines of the bridge and superstructure were definitely old-fashioned. I'd guess she was built maybe seventy-five years ago. But that's only a wild guess."

"She could have been sunk during the Spanish-American War," said Mr. Currier. "But no, there'd be a record if she were sunk by naval action. Suppose I look into it? I'd really like to. You've guessed by now that treasure hunting is the great passion of my life."

"You know, Mr. Currier," said Chris with a laugh, "I was puzzled about how you knew so accurately what the requirements were for a good boat for diving. You've explained it yourself. You're a diver, too."

"Not really, Chris. The girls and I do some shallow water skin diving, with aqua lungs, but I've never been down deep, nor ever been in regulation diving dress."

By this time, the *Jolly Roger* had proceeded southwards through Biscayne Bay, leaving Miami astern, swallowed in a shimmering haze. Peter lay prone in the waist, squinting idly through a scupper at the cool, translucent world below. Larry was back at the wheel after a short relief, while Chris and Mr. Currier pored over charts. They passed Featherbed Bank and the beginning of the Florida Keys.

In brilliant moonlight, they crossed into Florida Bay, a shallow island-dotted part of the Gulf of Mexico, and with a fair breeze and a following sea, charged down on their destination.

With sails neatly furled and the engine purring quietly at half speed, they ghosted up the canal and docked just below the *Princessa*. Mona and Linda Currier ran down to catch the lines, calling compliments on the salty appearance of the *Jolly Roger*, and laughing over the name still painted on her trailboards, *Hannah P. Pettingale*.

CHAPTER 15

Refitting the *Jolly Roger* began at once. The Cahills' capital was dwindling fast, and Chris was anxious to revive his salvage business. They were not foolish enough to try to do everything themselves, as it would have taken them months. The characters they got to help them were a weird lot, but they had to take what they could get. Larry was reminded again of *Treasure Island*, and the crew of pirates so innocently recruited by Squire Trelawney for the *Hispaniola*.

The ship's carpenter they hired was the oddest of the lot. He had an extraordinary face, much too small for his immense skull. His hair was as coarse as rope yarn, and grew not only on his head, but on and in his ears, formed a thick stubble over his chin and neck, and blended into a fur mat on his chest. Out of this circle of hair peered a face the size of a child's, with small, half-closed, almost Oriental eyes, a flattened pug-nose, and a misshapen mouth which he kept half-open, revealing the absence of four front teeth. The body which supported this queer head and face was exceptionally strong. His long arms dangled far down his legs, and his back, without having a hump, was round as a shell. He must have measured a yard and a half from shoulder to shoulder. He told them he was called "Chips," and, when Chris asked for his last name, said, " 'Chips' will do. I'll take my pay in cash." He was a good carpenter, his rates were not high, and he did his work quietly, without intruding on the Cahills. Yet they never felt quite comfortable when Chips was aboard.

The rigger, Benjamin, was as different from Chips as the antique-looking *Jolly Roger* was from the sleek, modern *Princessa*. Benjamin was a talker. He would tackle any subject that happened to be around, anything from the aspect ratio of the *Jolly Roger's* rig to the French troubles in Morocco. Benjamin didn't always know a great deal about the subjects he would bring up, but no one could accuse him of holding back an opinion on that account.

He was also an inveterate liar. This habit was upsetting to Chris, but Mrs. Cahill offered a charitable explanation. Perhaps, like some men, she said, he told the truth except when the truth was unpleasant. If he embroidered his personal adventures, that might be only because his real experiences were dull; he knew it, and he wanted to make them more entertaining for his listeners' sake. As in other claims, Benjamin's right to the title of rigger was somewhat less than his performance would indicate, but he could do an adequate job if closely supervised.

Smitty, the last of the trio, was a derelict who claimed to have once been a blacksmith, and later a locksmith. He was small, almost delicate, with an old, sly, withered face. A more unlikely looking person to work with metals would be hard to imagine; but the gammon and hance irons he made for the *Jolly Roger* (all of whose fitting were non-standard and had to be specially made) were almost works of art. He made a masthead band, a clew iron and a jack iron which were strong without unnecessary weight, fit exactly, and were finished so neatly that even Mr. Currier's critical eye could find no flaw. Smitty was no talker, especially about himself, but he seemed to be anxious to ingratiate himself with the Cahills. Without request, he made a complete set of keys for all the cabin doors, none of which had been provided with a key. Mrs. Cahill thanked him, but was not won over. As she remarked to Chris, "I have nothing against the man but his face, which he can't help, though it wouldn't hurt him to try."

Larry was completely enraptured with the *Jolly Roger*. Her tall raking masts, handsome sheer, and long low sides were the very embodiment of his conception of a privateer or pirate. "There's piracy aplenty in the history of the bugeye," Mr. Currier said to him, "and shanghaiing and violent death, too. But the pirate's booty was illegal oysters, not precious jewels or golden ingots. Death came most often from a fouled dredge line, or maybe the handles of a run-away winch, not from cutlass or bullet. Some of the hard-case skippers of the bugeyes, in the days when Baltimore was a big immigrant port, used to lure new immigrants aboard, work them and beat them and turn them ashore unpaid at the season's end, depending on their victim's ignorance of the language and customs to keep them from appealing to the police."

"How did they ever get the name 'bugeye'?" Larry wanted to know.

"There are all sorts of theories on that," said Mr. Currier. "Some people believe the name came from the hawse holes cut in the knight-head, up in the bows, which are supposed to look like a bug's eyes. I think it may be a local corruption of the Scotch word 'Buckie,' which means 'oyster shell.' All of the bugeyes were originally oyster dredges. There's a boat with a similar sheerline used in Scotland and called a 'Buckie.' "

The great strength, low sides, shoal draft and weatherliness of the bugeye which made her ideal for oyster dredging were equally desirable for diving. The bottom was made up of nine logs, which originally must have been at least eighteen inches square. The keel was fifty feet long. These bottom timbers were shaped and hollowed with axe and adze, leaving them a foot thick at the stem and stern posts, and six inches thick along the keel. The topsides were of heavy strakes on white oak frames. The whole structure was incomparably strong, even to the interior of the one remaining cargo hold. Mr. Currier explained that bugeyes had to be heavy, because the sharp edges of the oysters dumped aboard would chew a lightly built craft to pieces.

The *Jolly Roger* had the traditional rig proportions of her type—proportions passed down by eye and hand rather than by mathematics, and preserved in builders' models rather than in blueprints. The mainmast was the same length as the deck; the foremast was the deck length plus ten feet, both masts raked or slanted back two inches to the foot. The outboard length of the graceful bowsprit equalled the beam, and the inboard end was the length of the "bury" of the foremast—the part below deck. All of these proportions were part of long tradition, and had hardly changed since the Civil War.

The *Jolly Roger* carried six sails when under full canvas. Starting from aft, they were the leg-of-mutton mainsail, foresail, and a main staysail which ran from the mainmast head to a point halfway between the deck and the foremast head; then the fore-staysail, an inner jib and an outer jib or jib topsail. The "long-head" under the bowsprit ended in a beautifully carved figurehead of an eagle, and the trailboards on either side were decorated with elaborate scroll-work. She carried a hefty power dory on stern davits, and a light dinghy on the cargo hatch.

Larry enquired of Mr. Currier about the extreme rake or backward tilt of the masts. "Raking masts make jibing easier than plumb or straight masts," Mr. Currier explained, "and you can drop the sails when you're running off the wind. The rake makes it easier to use the halyard tackles for hoisting nets or cargo—or salvaged treasure," he added with a grin. "Besides, you get more deck-room aboard with raked masts, because the spars and rigging are kept away from the midship area. The foremast is stepped well up in the bows, and the center of effort of the sail is redressed by raking the spar aft. If the mainmast were straight, it would strike right through the main cabin, which isn't too roomy at best. By raking it, the cabin is kept clear, and the center of effort is brought aft to preserve a balanced sail plan."

This utilitarian explanation of the romantically angled masts added rather than detracted from Larry's love for the *Jolly Roger*, and he could certainly see the advantages when they used the boat for diving.

Both Larry and Chris tried to get odd diving jobs to help meet expenses until the refit was finished, and they could go into business again. Larry's first tropical dive was made off a nearby Key, where there was a museum of sunken treasure and relics recovered from the bottom, and an underwater marine garden frequented by tourists who would ride over the gardens in glass-bottomed boats. Mr. Currier had sold some relics to the owner of the museum, and arranged for Larry to substitute for the regular diver on his day off.

Larry felt a little uncomfortable about being an underwater showman, fumbling around purposelessly on the bottom in order to give tourists a thrill, but he soon forgot these reservations about the job in the novelty of his first dive in crystalline tropical waters. It was everything he'd hoped for—a fairyland of coral, translucent jellyfish, the delicate tracery of sea fans, and shadowy caves from which undulated the feelers of langoustas. The stems of the marine grass stirred languidly in the agitated prisms of light filtered down from the wave patterns. Bright-tinted fish grazed in the rich pasturage of the sea-floor.

The fish accepted him and did not flee as he stirred up little gusts of seadust and exhaled his plume of silvery breath. The coral had a dangerous beauty, for its sharp edges could make ugly cuts, and there were whole beds of purplish sea urchins, the poisonous porcupine of the sea, bane of the bare-skin diver. There was even the wreck of an old ship (climax of the exhibition dive) but it didn't look at all as he expected. Instead of a romantically battered hulk, there was only a pile of rock ballast and scattered bits of wreckage, so encrusted with coral as to be unidentifiable except on close inspection. The hull had disintegrated completely. Other divers had removed everything of interest and then brought back a few odd items as romantic props. Normally Larry would have used a skin diving outfit in these warm shallow waters, but the proprietor of the museum insisted on full diving dress, as looking more romantic.

The number of large fish in these tropic waters made Larry and Chris a bit nervous at first. They were never bothered, largely because they took simple common-sense precautions. The local divers warned them that, if they cut themselves, they should get out of the water at once, before the blood could attract hungry customers. Shiny objects attract big fish, which is why fishermen troll bright spoons as lures, so no shiny metal was taken below. The brownish-green moray eel, which infests holes in coral and has jaws like a crocodile, is a good reason for not poking around in dark crevasses with bare hands. It is attracted by white, which is why tropical divers so often blacken their hands. The twenty-five foot manta ray, the giant squid and other sea life of unsavory reputation get a big play in movies and fiction, but you almost never read an authentic news story of attacks on humans. As a matter of fact, a human being is a pretty sizeable customer himself when he's below the surface; and the most dangerous moments are when the diver is getting in and out of the water, when he is comparatively helpless.

Sharks usually turn tail and run when a diver advances toward them. This goes for the renowned killer sharks—the tiger, hammerhead, white shark and mako —as well as the gentler varieties like the nurse shark, shovel nose and sand shark. Big fish are more likely to attack when the diver flees from them, but most attacks are made by the rare rogue sharks, especially of species like the white shark, which have gone as much as 20 feet long.

"How do you tell all the different species of sharks apart?" Larry asked Mr. Currier.

"It's not easy," was the answer. "Take the white shark for example. He's dangerous. But he looks very much like the blue dog shark or the mako, which are less dangerous. The main difference is in the teeth. The blue dog and the mako have slim, catlike teeth, while the white shark has a large array of double-edged, triangular teeth."

"That's fine!" said Larry. "That's just dandy! You tell them apart by the TEETH! Next time I see one down below, I'll just wander over and provoke him till he opens his mouth. If he has teeth like a cat, I win, and I can punch him in the nose and chase him away. If the dental inspection shows those handsome triangular teeth you talk about, I lose, and he takes away my head or whatever part of me looks appetizing. This is sure a handy piece of information to have!"

"Why not feed the sharks in advance with garbage or something," wondered Peter. "That would blunt their appetites, like eating between meals. Reduce the temptation to snap up a tough morsel like Chris or Larry. The way they stuff circus lions with food before the liontamer goes in the cage."

"That would *really* fix things," said Mr. Currier. "A shark never stops being hungry. Dumping garbage overboard, fishing with a baited hook, or even throwing over a shiny tin can is like ringing a dinner bell for them. But the truth is you'll be bothered more by the less fatal pests; like the stinging jellyfish, sting rays, scorpionfish, sea urchins, or, particularly, the Portuguese man-of-war. Remember that their tentacles can be fifteen or more feet down from the body, and the sting hurts like blazes. Stay clear of them!"

"I will," promised Larry.

Chris was worried at the difficulty he was encountering in trying to set up a marine salvage business. He was turning over to his trio of semi-beachcomber ship workers many jobs which he and Larry and Peter could have done themselves, but he felt that they couldn't afford indefinitely living off their limited capital. They discovered that most coastal localities had got along without commercial divers for a long time, and it was quite a task for the Cahills to convince people that many jobs could be done more quickly, more cheaply, and better by having a diver. The Florida Keys had no lack of skin divers of various types, most of them amateur, and most of them devoted primarily to spear fishing or treasure hunting. But they often undertook easy salvage jobs at cut rates, making it hard for anyone to establish a regular business.

Chris covered a lot of ground by rented car, for he

had discovered that mail offers did not produce jobs. His friendliness and obvious sincerity gradually wore down some of the wary and reticent old timers, most of whom looked askance at strangers and divers as "more of them durn fool treasure hunters." They began to offer Chris information on the location of this or that piece of equipment lost "in the big storm of thirty-seven" or some other memorable disaster. Chris kept a record of these, for future use, but he needed immediate jobs of a less speculative nature.

There were some big salvage companies in the area, too, and Chris found that making friends among them paid dividends. There were many jobs with which the bigger companies wouldn't bother, which were easy for the Cahills: recovering outboard motors, locating lost moorings or clearing fouled anchors, raising small boats, clearing propellers. On some, like hull inspection and pier work, where the diver does not have to bend over or lie down, they could dive with just a helmet.

In this method, the helmet is lowered in an upright position and submerged until the exhaust valve is under water. The pump is started, the exhaust valve tested for leaks, a descending line and weight and a diving ladder placed in position. The diver goes down the ladder and ducks his head under the water and into the helmet, at the same time putting his left arm through the loop of the air hose, and his right through a loop of the line. He holds down the breastplate with his left hand and the descending line with the right hand.

This method of diving is inherently dangerous at any considerable depth, since it's hard to maintain equilibrium because of the great weight of the helmet and the buoyancy of the torso and legs. The air rushing into the helmet will keep the water level low enough for breathing, but there is danger of a diver in trouble losing his helmet, or even instinctively, when danger threatens, just ducking out from under the helmet, which is supported from above, and swimming to the surface. If the air has been under any great pressure, as from working at a considerable depth, air embolism could result. At thirty-three feet, the diver is breathing compressed air at twice atmospheric pressure. If the diver fills his lungs, throws off his helmet and swims up holding his breath, the air expands and exerts a pressure on the lungs of over 14.7 pounds per square inch at the surface. Since a pressure rise of only three pounds per square inch is dangerous for the lungs, the diver must ascend slowly and exhaust his lungs of compressed air before he reaches the surface.

The Cahills had a couple of shallow water face masks, with air fed from the surface, and one homemade self-contained rig in which the diver carried a tank of compressed air in a harness on his back. However, they did not trust this rig, and Chris finally decided that they had better discontinue helmet diving as too dangerous, and use either the shallow water masks or regulation diving dress.

They received one sizeable fee during this period, from the police, for recovering from Biscayne Bay a pistol with which a murder had been committed. At Larry's urging, this windfall was used to order from Lt. Cross of the Sparling School two complete self-contained diving outfits of a type which the Lieutenant had perfected. The waters off Florida and the Keys are warm enough for these rigs, except when diving in very deep water where they might have to stay down for a long period.

One afternoon, as Chris and Larry, just back from a diving job, were going over their records with Peter, Mr. Currier interrupted them with dramatic information. He had been making discreet inquiries through friends in the erstwhile Spanish islands, and he thought he might have identified the sunken ship Chris had stumbled upon in the Mona Passage. He was almost sure (no one could be certain) that she was the *Dona Isabella*, a Spanish steamer which had gone missing during the Spanish-American War, while trying to escape the American fleet. A considerable amount of bullion from Cuba had been in her storage room, and she had aboard as refugees several wealthy Spaniards who were returning to Spain. These people were believed to have carried as much as possible of their private fortunes with them. It was known that the master of the *Dona Isabella* had planned to sneak through the Mona Passage for a brief stop in San Juan before proceeding to Spain. She had been sighted at night by fishermen off Santo Domingo, and never seen again. Chris' description of the sunken ship he had seen was vague, but he agreed that the masts were rigged to carry auxiliary sail, the funnel was tall and raked like the *Dona Isabella's*, and the size was about right.

An excited Larry was all for organizing a salvage expedition immediately, but he simmered down when Chris gave him a rough estimate of the probable cost.

Mr. Currier looked thoughtful, then said, "Look here, boys, I may have an idea on that later on, but first, I've got a proposition concerning that old frigate I told you about. Some of the stuff down there is much too heavy for me and the girls to handle. Why don't you help me with the *Jolly Roger?* We can work out an arrangement, or, if you prefer, I'll charter the *Jolly Roger* and pay you regular scale rates for divers."

Larry stared at Mr. Currier, with doubloons and pieces of eight shining out of his eyes. Mr. Currier noticed it, laughed, and shook his head, "No, Larry. Not what you're thinking. But you'll find it exciting enough—and profitable enough—I promise you. We could run down

South tomorrow in the *Princessa,* and you boys could look the job over. Then when the refit of the *Jolly Roger* is finished, we'll be all ready. What do you say?"

Before anyone could answer, there was a stumbling sound on the deck outside the companionway, followed by muffled curses. Mr. Currier was on deck in a flash, followed by the Cahills. It was their misbegotten crew of ship repairers: Chips, Benjamin and Smitty. They looked sheepish and confused and slightly guilty, but Benjamin recovered quickly. "Just stopped aft for our pay, Cap'n," he told Chris. "All through for today, and a good day's work is done. We'll have her shipshape in no time at all, no time at all!"

Chris paid them, and they all watched them as they departed at an unusually rapid gait. "Do you suppose they were eavesdropping?" he asked Mr. Currier.

"Looks like it, doesn't it?" was the reply. "I'd really be alarmed if there were treasure on my frigate. But it wouldn't do to have word of the *Dona Isabella* noised about. There are so many treasure-hunters around here that you've got to be secretive, or find yourself with half a dozen boats following you every time you cast off. I wouldn't trust that crew around a treasure, but they haven't money enough, and probably not sense enough, to trail us to the frigate. Certainly not for a few bronze cannon."

CHAPTER *16*

~~~~~~

The *Princessa* cast off shortly after dawn the next day, with Larry and Chris and the Curriers aboard. A rebellious Peter had been left behind with Mrs. Cahill. Chris had been feeling a bit uneasy about his three workmen since the night before, and felt that someone besides Mrs. Cahill should be aboard the *Jolly Roger* to keep an eye on them.

Mona Currier was at the wheel, anxious to show off the *Princessa's* paces to Chris—and, incidentally, to demonstrate her own boat-handling ability. After they had cleared the passage, Mr. Currier gave Mona a Northerly course. "I thought the frigate lay to the South," remarked Larry.

"Did I say that yesterday?" asked Mr. Currier, looking concerned. "That was foolish of me. The wreck does lie to the South, but I never go directly to it. I don't want to be followed. We'll head north, then west, pretending to be fishing. Then we'll gradually ease south, and speed up whenever we seem to have the water to ourselves."

They set out the tackle, and dropped the outrigger to fish. They trolled a little faster than was right for good fishing, but not so fast as to arouse the suspicions of any of the half dozen other boats moving on the unquiet blue sea. There was a flurry of excitement when Mona got a strike, expertly landed a five pound barracuda and blushed at Chris' unstinting praise. Then Chris himself landed a kingfish, to praise from Mona which seemed to Larry more appropriate for a record-breaking marlin than a twelve pound kingfish. He climbed the *Princessa's* short, heavy mast, ducked into one of the twin lookout rings, and looked out over the shoal water. A little later, while Mr. Currier pored over his charts at the wheel, and took many course bearings at points on shore, Linda joined Larry at the masthead.

"Don't want to intrude, but I've got to con the boat over the shoals," she told Larry.

"You're never intruding, even if you could on your own boat. I've never really seen these coral shoals before. Beautiful, aren't they?" Larry looked over the pastel tinted shoal patches in the deep blue of the sea.

"Beautiful—and deadly," said Linda seriously. "Those coral heads could rip the bottom right out of us, even though we're double planked."

Mr. Currier was leaning out from his pilot's seat and scanning the ocean for boats. Traffic had thinned out as they had moved South. Now there were only a couple of boats in sight: a sports fisherman on the horizon, almost rolling her outriggers under, bound off shore; and a black craft that looked like a commercial fisherman converted from an Air Force crash boat.

This was Larry's first experience of piloting by eye among coral shoals. He discovered that it was not as simple as he had imagined. With the sun high and behind them, and the surface rippled by a gentle breeze, the deep water looked dark blue from aloft, lightening in color as it shoaled. The edges of the reefs or isolated coral heads showed a brownish tinge, and over the broad reefs themselves the water was a glorious green. All this was easy. But when the wind disappeared, and especially when the sun became obscured by a big bank of cumulus clouds, all he could see was the reflection of the sky and clouds staring back at him.

Larry was full of sincere admiration for Linda's assurance as she called directions to her father. *La Princessa* threaded into a charming anchorage at the head of a long, narrow bay behind a pine-covered reef. They did not anchor, but proceeded toward what was apparently a small underwater pass through the lagoon. A heavy swell was setting in from the other side of the point, where the shoreline of the Key changed direction. Their approach had been sheltered by land. The reef was a stirring sight. As each great roller began to feel the bottom, increasing in height and getting thinner, it grew paler and paler in color; then a flash of white would appear as its long back, and suddenly the whole mass of unstable water would tumble over in a great cataract of pure white foam and rush across the reef.

Cautiously Mr. Currier guided the *Princessa* inside the reef. There was a dangerous shoal spot at one side of the pass where the rollers increased in speed before breaking, but Linda called the course in her clear young voice, and they avoided it without difficulty. On the leeward side of the reef, outside, they found their deliberately unobtrusive buoy—an inverted bottle made fast to a piece of wreckage below.

"Golly, Mr. Currier," breathed Larry as he descended to the deck, "how'd you ever come to find this spot anyway?"

"That pool back there is a favorite anchorage of

ours," explained Mr. Currier. "We explored the area inside the reef in the dinghy on calm days, and discovered the pass. It's a good fishing spot, and I've often gone through in the *Princessa* after we had charted the passage with a hand lead from the dinghy. That's why no one else has discovered the wreck, in spite of all the traffic. You have to come in to shore as if to anchor, and then you pass out through the reef into a kind of dead end. If we tried to make our way to sea from here, we'd hit the reef that sank the frigate. We have to go back the way we came, even though it looks as if we could run straight out. And if that black fisherman tries to run in here, he'll soon hang up on that same reef."

The black crash boat which had hung off at some distance from them, but never out of sight, was now creeping slowly in. As they watched, her skipper apparently became alarmed at the shoaling water ahead, turned back, then idled as three or four men made a great show of preparing to fish. "We'd better just fish ourselves till that fellow clears out," said Mr. Currier.

"Wouldn't it be fun if we really did find some treasure down there," said Larry, who was unable ever to forget completely the possibility of locating pirate gold. "If we could put a jet hose down there and wash away the sand," he continued as they streamed their fishing lines, "who knows what we might turn up?"

"You forget, Larry, that diving is an ancient profession," said Mr. Currier. "Sure, treasure is recovered. Our Treasury Department records in Washington show that over $15,000,000 was declared for tax purposes by amateur treasure hunters in Florida last year, and they believe that that's only a quarter of the recoveries. Most of it is undeclared. This is the 'richest' area in the world, if that is the right word, in sunken ships—all along the Keys down to the Florida Straits. These straits are the most logical route between the Atlantic and the Gulf of Mexico. They've been used ever since 1519, when Cortez first sailed from Havana to loot the riches of Mexico. In the intervening years, hundreds of ships have been dashed to pieces on the reefs along the Florida Keys.

"You've seen the chart, and how Marathon and Key Vaca are right where the line of keys swings from a north-south direction to an east-west. There's a line of coral reefs paralleling the keys. A ship feeling her way in from the open ocean through the Straits could easily miscalculate her position and find herself in these dangerous waters. And the northeasterly winds that prevail in the area would carry a square-rigger this way. Add the perils of hurricane, pirates and privateers and men-of-war, and it's easy to see why so many vessels ended on the reefs.

"So much for the bright side of the picture, from the point of view of the treasure-seeker, though not from that of those old mariners. The other side of the coin is the matter of contemporary salvage of treasure. If there were survivors, they'd certainly try to recover treasure from shoal water. They could do it, too. The old-timers knew quite a lot about diving. In fact, the history of diving gear goes back to the ancient Greeks." Mr. Currier was riding his hobby again.

"The earliest mention of diving is in Homer's *Iliad*, which was written 500 years before Christ. A character named Patroclus compares the fall of Hector's charioteer to the action of a diver diving for oysters."

"Do you mean to tell me they ate oysters then?" asked Linda. There was a mischievous glint in her eye. She loved her father dearly, but she also delighted in teasing him. "I've heard that the bravest man in the world was the first man to eat a raw oyster."

"Did they dive for anything besides oysters in the olden times?" asked Chris, who was genuinely interested.

"Certainly," said Mr. Currier. "In the past war, our Navy used 'frog men' to clear underwater defenses at Syracuse harbor, in Sicily. People thought that was extremely modern, but divers were used in that same spot 2,000 years ago, to destroy barriers put up to obstruct and damage the Greek war galleys. Alexander the Great used divers at the Siege of Tyre, too. In fact, that was one of the first underwater battles, with the Greek divers trying to destroy the barriers as fast as they were erected."

"I suppose they dove without equipment of any kind, like the South Sea pearl divers," said Chris.

"No, surprisingly enough, they had some devices for drawing air from above water—something like modern snorkels. Aristotle tells how great vases were submerged with the mouth down to keep out water, so the diver could stick his head inside to breathe. Of course, our modern diving methods only date from 1830, when the first complete dress and helmet, with an air valve and a pump, were invented by a man named Augustus Siebe."

"How do you remember all this?" asked Larry, honestly puzzled.

"It's just an off-shoot of my foolish hobby, which is sunken treasure," said Mr. Currier. "It's important to know what treasures might have been salvaged long ago, if you're not going to waste your time. There was enough knowledge and determination even in the seventeenth and eighteenth centuries for known treasure in shallow waters to be recovered, either with mechanical contrivances or the cheaper method of using enslaved native divers. No, Chris, only a few of the dozens of wrecks in shoal water along this coast have produced treasure, because so much of it was recovered at the time of the loss. Yet there is still the treasure reported in tax returns, and if the government is right, it amounted to 60 million last year from Florida waters alone. I don't know if I'm discouraging you

or encouraging you, but I doubt if we'll find anything
more valuable than bronze cannon in this wreck. Let's go
down and see—that black fisherman seems to be heading
away now."

They assembled their free diving rigs. The Curriers
had two aqua lungs, while Chris and Larry had the new
equipment ordered from Lt. Cross.

As the Cahills and the Currier girls prepared for the
dive, Larry suddenly collapsed in helpless laughter. Chris
turned a puzzled face toward him, but Larry was too con-
vulsed to talk, and could only point at Linda Currier.
That giggling miss obliged by turning her back. Like the
others, she was wearing a heavy woolen garment like long
underwear as protection against the stings of jellyfish, as
padding for the weights they carried, and as some protection against sharp coral rocks, many of them poisonous,
and from the porcupine-like sea urchins which cause
painful sores on contact. Linda had painted a grotesque
face on the seat of this outfit—to scare big fish away, she
said. They all wore sneakers under their swim fins to protect their feet, wrist compasses, depth gauges and water-
proof watches.

It was more play than work as the four of them
splashed around on the surface, testing their equipment
and examining the bottom. Then Linda folded herself
double, hands to her toes, and down she went, the others
trailing her rapidly beating, grotesquely finned feet.

Despite his training, Larry half expected to find a battered hull lying on its side with broken spars, tangled rigging and scattered wreckage lying about. But the frigate
had lain on the bottom two or three hundred years, and
the ravages of time had disintegrated its structure and cam-
ouflaged its skeleton with encrustations of living coral.
Only the telltale cannon disclosed the secret.

At first Larry and Chris stayed protectively close to

the Currier girls, but it was soon apparent that both Linda and Mona were able to fend for themselves. Larry made a hasty inspection of the pile of ballast rock and the cannon, looked up at the *Princessa's* clean hull above him, then lost himself in contemplation of the spectacular ocean floor suffused by a blue-green crystalline light.

In this boundless expanse, the surface of the water was his sky. He felt cut off from his own personality—like the first man on a strange planet. There was a feeling of tremendous power. He weighed so little that he could climb a perpendicular coral wall with a flip of his feet. He could glide or float suspended in the warm fluidity. All action took on the effortless pace of a slow motion moving picture. It was a vital, beautiful world—yes, and ferocious, too. Most of the plants were really animals—with insatiable appetites for other tiny animals. He could not without penalty touch or step on any soft, fuzzy or jelly-like object, for most of them could sting.

Standing on a white bottom of ground coral and sand, the reef stretched up and out before him, all alive with waving plumes and seafans. Rounded brain coral and sharp-spined urchins dotted the expanse. Then Linda Currier swam leisurely to him, grasped his arm, and motioned to him to follow. She led him to a strange undersea ravine, with cliffs and caves in whose crevasses grew coral fans and trees. Tiny, rainbow-hued fish hovered about them. Several black and gold angel fish swam confidently by, waving their fins in slow and perfect rhythm. A huge grouper, pinkish-brown, regarded them lackadaisically, then moved contemptuously away. Linda showed Larry a huge anchor, one fluke buried deep in a pinnacle of coral, the ring almost large enough to swim through.

As usual, it was Chris who reminded Larry that they had another mission besides sight-seeing. He pointed to the surface, and all four divers swam up, to be almost blinded by the brilliant sunlight of the air world.

Back on the *Princessa,* Larry and Chris discussed methods of lifting the heavy cannon and the anchor when they returned with the *Jolly Roger.* Mr. Currier decided that he'd like to take one of the cannon back on this trip, so Chris and Larry descended again, dug holes under one of the huge tubes with crowbars, and passed heavy lines under it. They surfaced, hooked on the heavy tackle from the *Princessa's* strongly stayed mast and moused the hook, then began to crank the winch. It was slow work, but finally they got the cannon off the bottom.

Long ocean swells combined with the great weight made the *Princessa* list far over. The cannon would rise off the ocean floor as the boat rolled, then fall back on the bottom. Larry went below once more to inspect progress. The coral encrusting the giant tube had almost severed the lines. He came up for heavy wire, descended, and straddled the cannon as he rigged up slings. The cannon continued to rise and fall with the wave motion, and Larry thought amusedly that he'd never dreamed that he would ride a bucking horse on the bottom of the sea.

They didn't attempt to bring the cannon aboard. Instead, they slung it with wire and chains alongside *Princessa's* keel, and prepared to head back to their base. As they glided slowly out into the ocean, Mr. Currier snatched up the binoculars.

"There's that black boat again," he said. "I think they're watching us. And I don't like to try any false courses with that weight below."

Nevertheless, they rigged up for fishing once more. They passed through a great school of tiny fish—millions of them, closely packed. On the edges of the school, the bait fish spattered the surface like rain as savage barracuda attacked. Their lures no sooner edged the school than all four rod tips went down and the scream of the reels against the drag told of the strength of the strikes. They landed fourteen fish before they passed the school.

There were no more strikes, and as they neared their base, they reeled in. The black fishing boat was well off, and as the sun went down, they saw her change course to the north. "Perhaps they weren't watching us after all," Chris remarked to Mr. Currier, who shook his head doubtfully, then grinned. "I'm acting as worried as if there really were a treasure down there," he said. "Just the same, I have a proprietary interest in that wreck, and those old cannon do have a value."

They maneuvered the *Princessa* into her berth behind the *Jolly Roger*. Chris and Larry inspected the rigging of the *Jolly Roger* to see what progress had been made during their absence. There was none. They looked enquiringly at Peter, who had come down to the quay to take a line. He shook his head. "The men didn't show up. Not one of them. No word, either."

"That settles it," said Mr. Currier. "They *were* eavesdropping the other night. They heard about my frigate, and probably about the *Dona Isabella*, too. They must have blabbed it to whoever owns that black fishing boat. I can understand them getting excited over the *Isabella*, with all my talk about bullion and wealthy Cuban refugees, but why should they bother following us now? I distinctly said that we were just going to raise cannon."

"I'm afraid you didn't mention the cannon in so many words, Mr. Currier," said Chris. "You just talked about raising heavy weights."

"In any case, Chris, I guess we'd better not wait for the *Jolly Roger* to be refitted. Let's charter a barge and tow it down to the wreck with the *Princessa*. I'm getting stubborn about those cannon."

Very early the next morning, the *Princessa* was moved alongside the *Jolly Roger*, whose heavy tackles supported the weight of the cannon and lifted it to the quay, where after a brief excited inspection it was covered with a tarpaulin. The mouth of the cannon was open, which Mr. Currier said indicated that the man-of-war had been cleared for action when she struck the reef, whether chasing an enemy or fleeing from one no one would ever know. Except when ready to fight, the muzzle would have been plugged with a tompion, to protect the bore.

There was no difficulty hiring a small barge, and the *Princessa* set out once more for the wreck. It was clear sailing, with no black boats hanging around to worry them. They anchored over the wreck. Chris and Larry had prepared chain slings to fit in the muzzles, over the trunions and the breeches of the cannon, so it was a matter of only a few hours before they had all of the ordnance as well as the antique anchor aboard the barge.

There were two good reasons for speed. One was the reappearance of that same hovering fishing boat, this time much closer. The other was the weather, which was turning threatening. As the *Princessa* chugged protestingly through the pass, the wallowing barge behind, they became worried at the size and speed of the seas. A thin gray pall had spread over half the sky, and a hard line of clouds moved slowly up from the horizon. It was a whole new weather front. The seas which were running before the storm were already giving the *Princessa* trouble. Chris rigged the heavy canvas cover over the forward cockpit, which was right in the bows. When he returned to the bridge deck, he watched the heavily laden barge a moment, then shook his head at Mr. Currier. "We may have to cast off that barge before it carries away the quarter bitts," he said.

"Those bitts will never carry away," said Mr. Currier. "Trouble is, they're too far aft for a heavy tow. The barge is steering us—I have to use the engines as well as the rudders to keep on course." Any tow line that's carried to the stern of the towing vessel is likely to act like an extra rudder, which is why tug boats have their towing bitts almost amidships, at the turning point.

The weather grew slowly worse; the strange fishing boat was clinging to their flank like a harpy; the barge was yawing at the end of her double tow lines. It was not a comfortable situation. Mr. Currier was having more trouble controlling the *Princessa* now. He asked Chris to take a look in the bilge. It was full of water. The heavy drag and jerking of the barge was loosening *Princessa's* whole transom. She was leaking.

As Mr. Currier turned on the electric bilge pump, there was a heavy crash forward. A giant comber had crashed over their bows and torn the forward cockpit cover right out of its grommets. The cockpit was full of water, putting *Princessa* down by the bows. She fell off before the racing seas. Another sea came aboard, before the first one had time to drain out of the self-bailing scuppers.

Mona pointed at the companionway door leading from the cabin into the forward cockpit. Water was streaming through new cracks in the door. While they watched, another sea struck. The door splintered into fragments, and solid water poured into the cabin. *Princessa* had her bow under water and was unable to lift it out. Mr. Currier spun the wheel and reversed one engine, but with the bow down, both propellers high, and the great weight of the barge astern, *Princessa* wouldn't turn.

They had a minute, or perhaps a minute and a half, before the *Princessa* foundered. Larry sprang for one quarter bitt, Chris for the other, both struggling to open their jackknives. Mr. Currier was shouting to the girls to get into life jackets as the Cahill boys sawed at the twin tow lines. They parted, and *Princessa* came slowly about, half foundered, but safe. All hands bailed or pumped as Mr. Currier ran before the breaking seas. Mercifully, the engines kept running. With the wind screaming into the open bridge deck, *Princessa* staggered along until they had the water almost down to the floor-boards. Watching his moment, Mr. Currier brought the wounded *Princessa* about and headed once more into the storm, fighting their way to shelter. She almost capsized when they came about, but recovered just in time, as crockery and other equipment crashed from racks and shelves below.

Princessa was leaking badly, no doubt about it, but by pumping steadily they were able to hold back the gushing water. Larry spared one quick glance back at the barge. It was far astern, and the crew of the black fishing boat, which was twice the size of the *Princessa*, was trying to get a line aboard.

Gradually, the *Princessa* fought her way in to more sheltered waters, and Mr. Currier opened the throttles a little. They ran down the leeward side of the key, passed their safe slip, and brought her up to a nearby shipyard, where a gasoline pump was rigged to keep her afloat until she could be hauled out. It was a wet, bedraggled, unhappy crew that straggled back to the *Jolly Roger*, where Mrs. Cahill made clucking noises over the woebegone girls and scolded the men even before they had a chance to tell their story.

The Curriers doubled up with the Cahills in the *Jolly Roger*, with Larry, Chris and Mr. Currier sleeping in the saloon settees. As they sat up late that night discussing the incident, Mr. Currier brushed off the Cahill boys' attempts to commiserate with him.

"It's my own fault. I should have cast off the barge

sooner. But the *Princessa* is fully insured. We won't be able to use her for a while, or live aboard, but the repairs won't cost me anything. And I have a proposition I've been turning over in my mind for some time. I can advance you the money to complete the *Jolly Roger's* refit. We'll pay good rates and get honest workmen, not pirates like that other lot. Then we can all sail the *Jolly Roger* down to the Mona Passage and we'll see if Chris' sunken ship really is the *Dona Isabella*. If it is, we're rich. If it isn't, I've lost my investment for expenses, while you've lost some time, but you'll have your ship in good order. What do you say?"

"I say yes" exclaimed Larry, delightedly.

"How about you, Chris?" asked Mr. Currier.

"I don't know," said Chris. "We'd have to consult Mother and Peter. And it does seem like chasing a rainbow. We've all been loaded to the gunwales with treasure talk ever since we came to Florida, Mr. Currier. We've got to settle down some time if we're going to establish a business."

"Think it over, Chris. We could go to Mayaguez in Puerto Rico first. You liked Puerto Rico when you were there, didn't you?"

"I loved it," said Chris simply. He looked thoughtfully at a framed photograph of a group of stalwart Coast Guardsmen tacked to the bulkhead over the chart table. Chris' own face peered out of that picture. "I wonder if any of my old buddies are still stationed there."

Larry turned to Mr. Currier. "We're going," he said with absolute conviction. Chris did not contradict him.

CHAPTER *17*

~~~~~~

Mr. Currier was not content to let the missing barge just disappear. He made inquiries, and finally located the home port of the black fishing boat. While Chris and Peter studied the many problems involved in getting the *Jolly Roger* ready for the long sail to Puerto Rico and for the serious salvage attempt on the *Dona Isabella*, Mr. Currier and Larry drove up to find out if the fishermen had managed to recover the barge and cannon. They would have salvage rights, of course, but Mr. Currier could still regain the barge and its contents by paying the salvage claim.

The fishing boat was called the *Wrangler*, and she was the dirtiest and most untidy craft Larry had ever seen. Mr. Currier hailed her from the dock. The face that popped out of the companionway was Max Gsovski's.

Larry, who hadn't seen Max since their encounter in the restaurant six weeks before, managed a feeble "Hello, Gsovski," but was answered only by a glare. Gsovski mounted the companionway, followed by Chips, Benjamin and Smitty, the Cahills' three former shipworkers.

The last man to come on deck was apparently the Captain, beyond question a man of strong, if unsavory character.

No, he hadn't been able to save the barge, he told them. She drifted off and sank, Lord knows where.

There was little Larry or Mr. Currier could do without finding the barge, so they departed, feeling the unfriendly stares on their backs as they crossed to their car.

"About how much do you suppose those cannon were worth?" Larry asked Mr. Currier.

"Not a great deal, but not too little to steal, Larry. Their value is mostly as curiosities or museum pieces. They weren't all bronze—the bronze cannon would have scrap value. Probably $5,000 all told, including the barge. I think those fellows saved them, but they might as well be at the bottom of the Gulf Stream for all the good they'll do us."

The refitting of the *Jolly Roger* took on new drive with the help of the skilled craftsmen Chris hired with money advanced by Mr. Currier, though Mrs. Cahill insisted that there should be no round-the-clock work. She declared that she didn't intend to set sail with an exhausted crew. In the evenings, after work, all hands sat around the waist of the ship, watching the tropical sunset through the lacework of the palms, talking quietly of all possible subjects, but mostly of ships and the men who sailed them, of storms and pirates and treasure, of odd people one or another of them had met and odd places they had been. Mr. Currier was in his element, dispensing his encyclopedic knowledge with ease and wit.

One topic of never-failing interest was their destination, Mona Island, and its romantic history. Mr. Currier told them of his own searches on the island for Captain Jennings' treasure, and of the Pirates' Cavern which he had ransacked so diligently as a boy. Mona Island is a small dot on the chart, totalling perhaps ten thousand acres, near the middle of the Mona Passage between Hispaniola and Puerto Rico. It belongs to Puerto Rico. The island was thrust up from the ocean floor in three great prehistoric upheavals, leaving three distinct strata of rock honeycombed with so many caves that no one has ever counted them. In one of these caves, the Welshman William Jennings had hidden his loot.

The story is well documented, as pirates treasure tales go. Jennings was a rich man to begin with, and no one ever knew quite why he took up a buccaneering career. His biggest coup came in 1714, after the Spanish plate fleet of that year was wrecked by a hurricane. Many of the galleons went down in shallow water, and the Spanish authorities began salvage operations immediately. Jennings decided to raid the salvagers. He sailed over on his new sloop from Jamaica, found 350,000 pieces of eight neatly stacked on the beach, drove off the guards, and sailed away with the loot before the Spanish men-of-war could catch him.

Jennings sailed to deserted Mona Island, and buried the treasure in one of the deepest of the caverns. According to tradition, after locating the proper cave, the searcher must follow many deep and devious underground passages until he comes to a place where a dark stream runs over a sheer wall, leaving a dry grotto underneath. The cave now known as the Pirates' Cavern has been searched many times, by the then-youthful Nemesio Currier among others, but there are so many deep and dangerous passages that no one has ever claimed to have explored them all. "When you are deep inside the cavern," Mr. Currier told them, "you can hear a faint distant sound, like running water, but no one to my knowledge has ever found the stream."

"What happened to Jennings in the end?" asked Chris. "I suppose he was hanged like most of them."

"No, Jennings was one of the few who died peacefully in bed," said Mr. Currier. "He reformed late in life, and won the King's Pardon. He died a rich man, but then, he had been rich even before he took up pirating."

"Seems likely he recovered his own treasure, just the same," said Chris.

"Perhaps," agreed Mr. Currier. "But it's said that his contemporaries believed he had not lifted it, and watched him so closely that he was never able to get back to his treasure vault before his death. The theory is that his fellows would be able to guess pretty accurately whether or not he had possession of that much wealth. Anyway, it is one of the most believed-in treasures in the West Indies."

"My own plans are settled," announced Peter. "While Chris and Larry are groping around among the sharks and barracuda, I'll just dig up Mr. Jennings' little piggy bank."

"Wait till you start counting the caves on Mona Island," laughed Mr. Currier, and Chris remarked: "While Larry and I are groping around with the fish, you'll be up on deck tending lines and watching the air pressure, or I'll know the reason why!"

CHAPTER 18

Total refit of a boat is never entirely completed. There always remains something more to be done. But there came a day when the *Jolly Roger* was considered sound in hull and rigging and engine room. Remaining tasks could be accomplished by her crew while en route.

Ostensibly, they were sailing for the Bahamas, and Larry made a great show of buying charts and sailing directions for those islands from the local marine supply house. Charts of the Greater Antilles were ordered by mail. Despite their conviction that Chips and Smitty and Benjamin knew about the *Dona Isabella*, they still felt it wise to conceal their destination.

In the still dawn, the *Jolly Roger* backed out of her slip. There was little wind, but everyone agreed that such a voyage as this was to be should be started under sail. While the diesel engine purred like a well-cared-for cat, Linda Currier took the wheel. They made sail, hoisting the mainsail first and then each sail in turn, working forward.

As the sun rose behind the palmettos, a light zephyr came from the southwest. Chris killed the engine, and there was no noise but the swish of the water from the bows, a small seething sound under the turn of the bilge, an occasional creaking from one of the blocks. The *Jolly Roger* was under way for Mayaguez in Puerto Rico, with the old pirate haunt, Mona Isle, as port-of-call to pick up treasure!

The impersonality of the sea turns the sailor back to the warm personalities of his shipmates, and gives him an abiding love for the ship that so gallantly carries him. The friendship between the Cahills and the Curriers grew deep and solid in this period. They came to understand one another without speech, to make allowances where necessary without feeling a sacrifice.

And they worked. Not in a frenzy, but calmly and competently. The accomplishment of simple things was intensely satisfying, as the ship rolled on under a clear blue sky. Chris was busy overhauling the all-important compressors or air pumps. They had two complete outfits, each consisting of a gasoline pump to compress the air, a pressure tank on deck to even out the air supply pulsations and act as an air reservoir in case of failure of the pump, and an emergency air tank. Valves and gauges were provided so that topside personnel could regulate the pressure. They also had a small recompression chamber, an item insisted upon by Chris, since their work would be in deep water and would involve the tricky and dangerous business of actual entrance into the wrecked ship, from which a rapid ascent might become necessary. Chris wanted to take no chances with the "bends."

Mr. Currier worked at small jobs of rigging and ship-fitting. Mona and Linda and Mrs. Cahill became adept with the sailor's palm and needle, while Larry and Peter dragged out the diving dress and overhauled it. All this was done under the spell of the blue tropic seas, the quiet power of the sails, the swi-s-s-h of the waves, the ascending architecture of the clouds. Sometimes they would lift their voices in song, but the real and constant background music, of soft strings, great woodwinds and murderous percussion, was the sea—the beautiful, brawling, merciless sea.

One thing they all did on the trip, in calm weather, was to think. What about? Not about petty details of living, not about the recurring world crises. They mused most often about the sea and the men and ships that sailed it. It was a rich subject. How did seafaring men first learn that copper and bronze and iron don't mix in a ship's fastenings, that electrolysis will eat them away? What dire happening finally convinced the mates of early merchant ships that heavy cargo must not all be stowed on the bottom, that some of the weight must be spread aloft if the ship is not to roll her masts out? Who first discovered that excessively heavy and tight stays and shrouds can weaken —indeed, break a spar by compression? What genius invented the bowline? How many ships burned before the awful mystery of spontaneous combustion was revealed?

They talked, of course, and a lot of the talk, naturally, was about treasure.

"How about these magnetic or electronic gadgets that show you where metal is?" asked Larry. "Don't they make treasure hunting a lot easier?"

"They certainly would—if they'd work," said Mr. Currier. "Mind you, I don't say that some devices won't operate under certain conditions, but it's not as easy as it seems. I spent a lot of time and money experimenting with an electronic metal locator that would work in sea water. To tell you the truth, it was a complete flop."

"You can buy war surplus mine detectors pretty cheaply, can't you?" asked Chris.

"Yes, but they're basically unsuitable," said Mr. Currier. "Magnetic fields, not electromagnetic waves, should be used, with either low alternating frequencies or pulsed direct current. In principle, it's all very easy. But sea water is a conductor as well as a metal object in it. The trouble with detection instruments is that they are seldom sensitive enough to detect the difference in conduction between the two. In shallow water, a glass bottomed viewing box is the best searching instrument. Another trick I've seen worked is to pour a little olive oil on the water on a calm day. If you do it right, you can see the bottom a long way down. But the best way of all is to swim around on the surface with a face mask, preferably one with a snorkel."

"Anyone who pours any of my olive oil on the water will go on a diet of hard tack, or else get seawater instead of oil in his salad," said Mrs. Cahill grimly.

Slowly but inexorably the path carefully pricked out on their charts approached their destination. And then early one morning, coming on watch, Larry put his head out of the ship's companion, and saw ahead a high green mound rising out of the sun-crimsoned waters. Mona Island! To come thus into the lee of land after an open water passage is to enjoy a thrill which ranks high among life's experiences. The landfall is the height of the sailor's accomplishment. It is the culmination of all his efforts, preparation and work. The seaman's entire reason for existence is his ability to make a landfall.

The pungent, rich and sweet aroma of the land after the austere salt air is a heady potion. They all went a little mad on the schooner, as they smelled the earth, with flowers, grass, trees and other ingredients blending into a flavor no sailor will ever forget. They came into the lee of a small cove, and then there was that most pleasant of sounds, the rattle of an anchor chain when you've reached your harbor.

CHAPTER *19*

~~~~~~

They woke to the pelt of tropical rain on the decks and the overhead. What of it? For the first time in many days, they enjoyed the luxury of staying in their bunks until the last desire for sleep was worn out. Mrs. Cahill and the girls built a fantastic breakfast, since time was of no consequence and they weren't going anywhere. And how they savored it! Then when the steady drum of the rain changed to a patter and later just an occasional splash from the rigging, out came the hot sun, steaming decks, the smell of drying.

Briefly they debated the advisability of a turn ashore, but although they were all hungry for the feel of land and the chance to explore the jagged cliffs and romantic coves of the island, both Mr. Currier and Chris agreed that it would be wiser to make a quick search for the *Dona Isabella*, and, if they located it, to proceed to Mayaguez for the final stages of their salvage preparation. To linger at Mona now was to excite local curiosity, which they were particularly anxious to avoid.

Chris and Larry mapped out the searching technique

they would use. Chris had the bearings of the wreck, obtained by mail from friends in the Coast Guard stationed at Puerto Rico. Once the Coast Guard has proof of a previously unknown or unlocated wreck, no matter how old, it goes down in the records. But such a bearing is necessarily only an approximation when measured by the slow pace and limited visability of a diver. An elaborate search map and procedure must be worked out, to prevent gaps in areas searched, or searching the same area more than once.

Fortunately, the weather was calm after the morning rainstorm, though the current was swift. They located their spot as nearly as possible, and anchored the *Jolly Roger* bow and stern. They searched first with self-contained rigs and foot flippers, as they could cover the bottom more rapidly that way. There was no sign of the *Dona Isabella* in the shallower water close to the island.

The bottom shelved off sharply on the Hispaniola side, and so they ascended, moved the schooner, and descended again in regulation pressure diving dress. There were a great many barracuda about, and several sharks, including one enormous customer with implacable little eyes.

They searched all afternoon without success, using the circular method at first, and then changing because of the heavy current to a back-and-forth pattern across the tide as far as they could reach with their distance lines. Larry was about ready to quit when Peter's voice came over the phone. "Chris thinks he sees something. He wants you to come over."

This was electric news. With Peter guiding him over the telephone by the location of his and Chris' current borne air bubbles, Larry stumbled over the rough bottom until he located Chris. When Larry joined him the brothers put their helmets together so they could talk. "Be careful the current doesn't carry you over the cliff. Look over while I hold your life line," said Chris.

A sharp abyss fell away a few yards from where the divers stood, and a strong current on the sea floor streamed toward it like a river flowing toward the crest of a waterfall. Cautiously Larry worked his way to the edge and peered down. At that depth, visibility was limited, but through the dim green light he could see the top of a mast and a tall funnel. In his excitement, Larry leaned dangerously over the cliff to try to make out the hull, but a sharp tug by Chris on his life line brought him back. Chris pointed up, and both divers worked their way back to prepare for an ascent. They would have to move the *Jolly Roger* closer to the wreck before seeking her deck. This was going to be a very deep dive. They were already at 90 feet. Assuming the masts to rise only one hundred feet above the decks of the sunken steamer, they would have to work at 200 feet, perhaps even more.

Strain from the excitement of their find, added to the normal fatigue of a dive, left both Chris and Larry quiet and uncommunicative, to the annoyance of the others, but their tense nerves gradually relaxed, and they began to talk. "Those masts certainly look as if they had once been rigged to carry auxiliary sail," said Chris. "Wasn't that unusual, as late as 1898?"

"Then it must be the *Dona Isabella*," spluttered Mr. Currier. "It was quite common for small steamers to carry sail in the late nineteenth century, though it was unusual around the turn of the century. The *Dona Isabella* was built in 1872, so she was twenty-six years old when she sank. She had steel masts, with fore and aft sails. This has to be she!"

"Is there any other identification we can make?" asked Larry. "Any peculiarities in her superstructure?"

"Yes," said Mr. Currier, who had made detailed inquiries. "She had three decks above her main deck, a large poop deck for immigrant passengers, and her funnel has quite a rake, which was exceptional in those days. Most of the funnels on the early ships were almost plumb—went straight up and down. If this funnel is raked, then it's the *Dona Isabella*."

"I couldn't say whether it was raked or not," said Chris, shaking his head. "Could you, Larry?"

"I'm not sure," said Larry. "I think maybe it was, but it's hard to tell from the angle we were looking at her. We'll have to go down again to be sure."

On the following morning the *Jolly Roger* was moved right over the wreck. Chris and Larry descended again, the former to explore the area around the ship and determine whether there were other cliffs or natural hazards below. Larry went down his descending line, close to the foremast of the steamer. Then his lead-soled boots hit the deck of the ship. He was the first man to tread those decks in half a century!

Watching his lines and moving carefully, he stepped slowly along the slippery deck, which was cluttered with bent and broken boat davits, smashed rails and other debris. This was a bad place for fouled lines. He was careful to keep a secure hold on some part of the wreck whenever he could, so that the current wouldn't drag him off the vessel. He couldn't hold onto objects over his head, because he was diving without gloves, and raising his arms too high would permit air to escape out of his cuffs, and cause him to lose his positive buoyancy, with resultant danger of falling. Edging his way over the engine room fiddley, at the foot of the funnel, he measured with mounting excitement the angle of the funnel with the deck. There was no doubt. The funnel slanted back. He reported his findings to Peter over the telephone.

"Take it easy, Larry," cautioned Peter. "You sound

excited. That's bad in that depth. Stay where you are till you calm down a little." Peter was developing into a first rate topside man.

In a few minutes, after Peter had observed that Larry's air bubbles were again coming up in a steady stream instead of the irregular clusters that indicate excitement or fear, he called Larry again. "Mr. Currier wants to know if you can count the decks?"

Larry worked his way to the lee side of the ship—lee, in terms of the heavy current—and called back, "I'm going to drop down her side and count the decks. Stand by to give me line. By the way, this ship has no well-deck, and she carried two lifeboats on each side of her midship house. Is that right for the *Dona Isabella?*"

"Never mind," answered Peter. "You just report what you see. We'll talk it over later. But you'd better wait till I can lower you a Jacob's ladder. Too risky just to drop down. I'll feed you your line slowly. Don't take any chances."

Larry worked over to a break in the rail, put one hand on his air valve to regulate pressure, and held the other ready to fend off from the side of the ship, which angled slightly away from him. When the weighted Jacob's ladder reached him, he fastened it in place, got his feet firmly on a rung, and instructed Peter to lower him. Slowly he crept down the ship's side, counting the rows of port lights. One row; another; a third. Three decks. Then a stunning discovery. There was a fourth row, together with a cargo door, indicating a fourth deck. If the cargo door opened on her main deck, then she had four, not three decks above, and was not the *Dona Isabella*. If the cargo door was in a deck below the main deck, then the fourth row of ports could indicate the main deck, and it could still be the *Dona Isabella*. He reported his findings to Peter, telling him, "I'm going to work my way aft.

When I get to the after cargo hatches I'll see if I can count the decks from astern, and I can check the size of the steerage."

"No you won't," said Peter firmly. "You've been down long enough. Chris has already checked the steerage. You're both coming up."

No diver in his right mind argues with his handler when he's on the bottom. The topside man keeps a detailed time log on the whole diving procedure, to determine the length of time and number of stops to decompress in the ascent. Peter's log recorded the time Larry entered the water, when he started down, when he reached the wreck's deck, when he was on the bottom, and he had a regular schedule of depths and times which must be rigidly adhered to on the ascent to avoid "bends." Mona Currier was keeping a similar log on Chris, while Mr. Currier tended Chris' lines.

It was an interminable trip up to the surface, but Larry had to school himself in patience. Finally, he broke surface, followed almost at once by Chris. Then there was an excited discussion as they exchanged notes. Everything indicated that this was the *Dona Isabella* except the uncertainty about the number of decks in her main superstructure. Chris thought there were three, but wasn't sure. Mr. Currier thought it unlikely that a ship that small would have four decks, and was confident that Larry had mistakenly counted the main deck as well as the three above it. While they debated they noticed a good-sized schooner, close hauled on the port tack, approaching them.

"She's probably an island schooner for Trujillo City or San Juan," said Mr. Currier. "I guess she's curious about us."

"If I could go down once more, I could make sure," said Larry. "We still have enough daylight."

"Are you crazy?" demanded Chris. "You know we can't make more than one dive in twenty-four hours to that depth. Lt. Cross would take a paddle to you if he knew you even suggested it. Neither one of us is going down before the day after tomorrow. Let's get the down lines and stages up, and move off this spot before that schooner comes abreast and sees we've been diving."

Anchored in such depths, it took a long while to get the stern anchor aboard, and they were still at the windlass cranking up the bow anchor as the strange schooner beat her way alongside. She ran up the colors of the Dominican Republic, as the *Jolly Roger* streamed the Stars and Stripes. There was a brief exchange of staccato Spanish between Mr. Currier and one of the men on the Dominican schooner.

"He wanted to know if we're in trouble, anchored here," explained Mr. Currier. "I told him we were cruising yachtsmen out fishing, and he suggested we move up the passage to shoaler water. Too deep here for fish, he says."

"Not for the kind of fishing we want to do," said Peter. "Where to now, Skipper?"

"Mayaguez. No use wasting a whole day here. I'm satisfied it's the *Dona Isabella*. If it isn't, we might as well have a look at it anyway, now we're on the scene."

CHAPTER *20*

~~~~~~

Larry's excitement reached fever point as he set foot on the quay at Mayaguez. This was his first experience in a foreign atmosphere. The bustling city was a series of contradictions; of impressive modern structures mingled with pastel-tinted Spanish casas; broad paved avenues with narrow cobblestoned streets leading from them that reflected all the romance of colonial Spain.

Mr. Currier acted as guide and interpreter for the Cahills, with eager interruptions from Linda and Mona, who knew the city well. He had many tales of the past. Only a few miles from Mayaguez, at Aquadilla, Christopher Columbus had landed on his second voyage, in 1493. As they admired the Cathedral, Mr. Currier told how the pirate Kofresi, whose base was Mona Isle, one day had seen a beautiful Spanish girl entering to attend mass. She was the most lovely thing he had ever seen. A man of quick and violent emotions, he had fallen madly in love with her at sight. Barred by his reputation from a normal courtship, he kidnaped the señorita and fled with her in his ship.

They made first for Mona, but since every vessel in the harbor put to sea in pursuit, Kofresi left Mona and had his crew deposit him and his lovely captive on a lonely island off the Caribbean coast, Caja de Muerto. There they lived, until the death of the maiden, whether by illness, by her own hand, or by her abductor no one ever knew. The pirate was captured and hanged, but insisted to his death that it was an elopement and not an abduction, and that the girl had died of natural causes.

"What does 'Caja de Muerto' mean?" asked Larry.

"Dead Man's Chest," answered Mr. Currier with a grin. "That's really its name. You've heard of it if you've read *Treasure Island*."

Mr. Currier arranged for local guards to stay on the *Jolly Roger*, as he planned to visit friends and relatives. He wanted the girls to stay with him, but they insisted on going to San Juan, the capital, with the Cahills.

The trip to San Juan by *publico* (public automobile—a sort of inter-city taxi cab) was a delightful experience. The weather was perfect. Of all the sun-drenched Caribbean islands, Puerto Rico is most blessed in climate. The sun is hot, but the Northeast trade winds blow endlessly during the day, and the land breeze from the mountains cools the night.

Next morning, Chris and Peter left the party at the hotel to check at the hydrographic office, the Coast Guard base, and then to see about obtaining explosives. Mona Currier took Mrs. Cahill under her wing, while Larry and Linda tramped the streets to see the sights.

Late that afternoon Linda and Larry walked back toward their hotel through the Plaza, hounded by a swarm of good-natured but persistent shoe-shine boys. Any reasonably well-dressed person whose shoes are one degree below brilliance will be trailed by a whole platoon until he comes to rest on a bench to have this serious flaw in

his appearance corrected. Larry picked a blonde-headed
urchin with an impish, freckled face. The youngster told
Larry and Linda that his name was José Figueroa, although his competitors called him *Rubio* or "Blondie."
José went to work with a theatrical flourish which was
truly Latin, while idle kids gathered to comment on and
criticize the job. Then Linda grabbed Larry's arm.

"Look," she said. "There's that fellow who was so
fresh in the restaurant, the night we met."

Larry looked up quickly. Sure enough, it was the
scowling visage of Max Gsovski. As he watched, Chips,
Benjamin, and Smitty appeared. They recognized Larry
with a start, and withdrew quickly into a cantina. Larry's
heart sank.

Linda told José Figueroa in Spanish to forget Larry's
shoes, pointed at the cantina, and gave him instructions in
rapid Spanish. José nodded, pocketed the coin Linda gave
him, and hurried to the corner, where he took up his station outside the swinging doors. "I told him to follow
the four Continentals when they leave the cantina, and
then come to our hotel and tell us where they went," she
told Larry.

The Cahills and the Currier girls dined at their hotel,
the Palacio. Before dinner was over, a message came up
from the desk. Linda went out and was back in a moment
with word from José. The four men had gone to a big
black motorboat moored at the inner harbor. There was
no room for doubt now. The Cahills had competitors in
the search for *Dona Isabella's* bullion. And unpleasant
competitors at that.

It was now imperative that they start diving operations without further delay. They left early next morning, accompanied by an old Coast Guard friend of Chris',
Chief Boatswain's Mate Maddox, an enormous hearty man.
Like many seamen and divers, the Chief bragged mightily

about inconsequential things, but did his bragging about his profession by understatement.

Larry asked him if he still did much diving, to which the Chief answered, "Oh, I go down once in a while," and Larry knew that he was in the presence of a master diver.

Through persistent questioning, Larry drew out some details of military diving, and learned that in wartime, a deep sea diver is a mighty important man. Chief Maddox asked questions of his own when he discovered that Larry was himself a diver, a graduate of the Sparling School, and that he had not yet performed his required military service. The Chief had a real recruiter's gleam in his eye as he expounded on the advantages of service in the U.S. Coast Guard, and related tales of his own wartime experience.

The deep sea diver is a tremendous national asset in time of war. If large scale trouble comes again, we shall be slightly better equipped in this respect at least than last time. The Sparling School alone has turned out over a thousand highly competent divers. In World War II, the clearance of underwater obstructions, reconstruction of harbor facilities, salvage of fighting ships and materiel rose to new heights. Eighteen divers cut away nets and placed explosives to clear the entrance to Casablanca in 1942. Five hundred vessels were raised out of the muck at Manila. From Pearl Harbor to Africa to Anzio to the Normandy Beachhead, the diver was a V.I.P. indeed. It is odd to think of American divers working in the same waters as the warriors of Alexander the Great, and on the same task, clearance of the enemy-laid obstructions to a mighty battle fleet.

In the event of war, all our harbors are potential targets of enemy attack. With the present development of military weapons, harbor destruction is possible on a scale which could cause a military debacle. Seaports capable of handling a large volume of shipping are few, especially on the West Coast. The marine clearance, salvage and construction task which would result from direct attack or underwater sabotage would present a tremendous task to civil disaster and military organizations. Recollection of Pearl Harbor is all the proof needed—and the weapons of attack are far more effective now.

Although the U.S. has many more divers today than at the time of Pearl Harbor, the number is far short of what would be required in all-out war. Since 1940, some 3,000 commercial and military divers have been trained. About 70 per cent of these were trained by the Armed Forces, 25 per cent by the Sparling School, and 5 per cent in commercial on-the-job training. Only a handful of the trained military divers remain in the service. About one hundred former military divers are now engaged in commercial diving, thus maintaining their skill. Of the almost 1,000 men graduated from the Sparling School, approximately 550 are actively engaged in diving. Thus, a critical need for divers will arise in the event of general war, and Chief Maddox told Larry that there was no better contribution he could make than to continue his profession when he went into uniform.

"You've got a lot better chance for a diver's rating in the Coast Guard than you have in the other services," he told him. "What's more, we can probably arrange for you to serve part of your time right here in Puerto Rico, if you want." Larry promised to think it over, when their present project was completed.

Once aboard the schooner, no time was wasted. As Chief Maddox left the ship, he told Chris, "Remember, if those laddies get rough, don't you try to fight 'em. Not with ladies aboard. Just pass the word along to me. We'll know what to do. Say the word, and we'll cruise by anyway, just to keep things in order and let 'em know you got friends." Chris thanked him, but asked him not to come by unless there was word from him. Chris was not yet ready to make an official declaration of his purposes, for he knew the electric way the word "treasure" spreads.

They reached Mona Island at sundown. In the brief twilight of the tropics, the black filigree of palm fronds ashore swiftly receded into the night. They sat on deck, watching the magic of these summer seas by moonlight, the whole heavens spread for their view, a school of porpoise scattering bright twinkles of phosphorescence in their wakes, the incredible grace of the gulls, the nostalgia of being anchored where pirates and conquistadores had preceded them.

CHAPTER 21

~~~~~~

With the first light of the new day, they proceeded to the inconspicuous buoy they had left over the *Dona Isabella,* and rigged up for diving. There was no sign of the black-hulled *Wrangler.*

The shelf on which the *Dona Isabella* lay was slightly over 230 feet below the surface—just below the level at which the reef-building coral can live. These tiny marine animals, whose skeletons have created so many reefs, atolls and islands, must have clean sunlit water, for heavy mud and sediment suffocate them. They are seldom found at depths beyond 150 feet. The decks of the sunken ship were about thirty feet higher. At the 200 foot level, Chris and Larry had to take two hours in the ascent to decompress after working less than an hour on the ship's deck. They were working at a pressure of 90.8 pounds per square inch, over six times the pressure at the surface. With so little working time on the bottom, it was essential that they inspect the wreck carefully and plan their work to the last detail.

They speculated on how the *Dona Isabella* had come

to grief, and guessed that she had run aground, but had not been badly smashed; that the Captain had managed to work her off at high water, but in the process had probably ripped a hole in her bottom, or strained the rivets so that a whole plate or series of plates had given away, and the ship sank like a stone.

The hull seemed undamaged amidships, and they were hopeful that they would not have to blast a way into the hull to find the strongroom where the bullion, if any, would have been locked up. Submarine blasts, even when the explosive is placed high on the vessel, have a way of blowing great holes in the sea bottom. Such a hole could easily make the wreck heel far over instead of sitting at only a slight list. The greater the angle of heel, the more difficulty in working inside. Improper placing of the charges could even ruin chances of recovering any possible treasure. Jagged plates torn off by the explosives would be the worst kind of hazard for the diver, who would have to work through the bulkheads, cabins and alleyways among growing mountains of debris.

In order to increase working time below, in view of their haste to complete the job before the *Wrangler* should appear, Larry and Chris dove in turn, each staying on the bottom two hours, with the other starting down as the first began his slow ascent to decompress. In case of emergency, the second diver was thus always ready to help the first, yet they got in four good man-hours of work on the bottom, which, with the final decompression time, meant that all underwater work would be completed and both divers out of the water in less than seven hours.

Larry went down first, to see if he could get inside the ship and locate the strongroom. It proved easy. The doors to the cabin opening on deck were unlikely to lead to the strongroom, which was probably well inside the ship. But Larry found one door, dogged down but not locked fast, which he managed to hammer open with a pinch bar from the sack of tools he had brought down with him. It led through a short passageway to what had been the main saloon of the ship. It was intensely dark inside, but he had an electric torch which shone fitfully through the water, which was clouded by the silt he had stirred up. There was no indication which stateroom might have been the purser's office, so he started checking one stateroom after another. The first was empty. The second door was jammed, but he forced it open with the pinch bar. The deck was tilted up from where he stood at the entrance, and opening the door made a strong swirl in the water-filled cabin. Larry flashed his torch around the stateroom. There was a double berth opposite him. Something was moving on the lower berth! An octopus? In such tight quarters, an octopus would be an ugly customer, and they loved wrecks.

But no. How could an octopus get into that cabin, which had been tightly closed for half a century? Larry shone the light on the berth again. It was no octopus. It was a man.

Larry staggered against the door, setting up another swirl. The man, who had been lying on the berth, as if he were taking a nap, instead of floating against the overhead like a normal corpse, sat up on the berth, then rose to the slanting deck, and walked half-crouching toward Larry, waving his arms in the water, as if about to spring. He kept coming at his immobilized victim, lank hair distended in the water, his terrible face half eaten away by fish. Icy shivers ran down Larry's back, his limbs were paralyzed, he had the stale, cotton-dry taste of blood in his mouth and the hot chug-chug of rivets in his brain. Then the thing was on him, pushing him back. In an explosion of horror and revulsion Larry thrust it away and forced the door closed.

Peter's voice was droning over the telephone inside his helmet, but he couldn't answer. He was dizzy, and could hardly stand. Peter was worried. His voice grew sharper—for the handler always gets concerned when his diver does not respond, particularly inside a wreck where the air bubbles and the angle of the life line and air hose give no clue to the diver's activities. "Chris is on the way," Peter was saying. "Answer me, Larry! Please answer! What's wrong? Chris is coming!"

At the same time, Larry could feel Peter's hand signals—two pulls, then one; two and one—telling him, "Answer the telephone." Then Peter switched to single pulls, meaning, "Are you all right?"

Finally Peter's desperate voice broke through Larry's stunned senses. His first thought was to get out. He mumbled to Peter that he was coming up, and that Chris should stay up. Then he stumbled out of the sunken ship to the green gloom of the deck, which seemed bright after the utter darkness inside the ship, except where his torch had shone.

Larry calmed down during the slow ascent. He knew it couldn't be a ghost. There was no such thing as a ghost. Yet it had been alive, had stared at him with that horrible eaten-away face, had moved to attack him!

Chris descended and met him at sixty feet. He put his helmet against Larry's, so they could talk, and demanded, "What happened?"

"There's a ghost down there," said Larry, feeling foolish as he said it, now that the shock was wearing off. "Anyway, it's a dead man, and he's moving on the deckplates, not floating against the overhead."

"Where is he? I'll go down," said Chris. Larry answered, "Wait a little bit and I'll go with you. Gave me an awful fright."

"You go on up," ordered Chris.

"No, I'm over it now," said Larry. "I feel like a fool. There must be a logical explanation. I'll feel like a coward if I go up. I've only been down an hour."

Peter, on the deck of the *Jolly Roger*, was demanding an explanation, and Larry could imagine the consternation of the others. "I just found a corpse and got rattled," he told Peter over the phone. "We're both going down again."

When Larry pointed out the stateroom door, Chris opened it slowly. The corpse was lying on the deck, but floated half-erect as the water stirred from the opening door. Chris grabbed it, and the two divers worked their way out of the ship, pulling the body with them. Larry called to Peter to send down a weighted line, and Chris told Mr. Currier over the phone, "We're sending up a corpse, and it isn't pretty. Better get the women below decks until you can cover it with a tarpaulin."

The mystery was solved when Chris and Larry got topside again. The corpse had been a small man, and he was wearing a money belt full of Spanish gold around his waist. It had ballasted the corpse like a diver's weighted belt, and by a freak chance was just right at that pressure to give him negative buoyancy, so that at any swirl of water he floated upright. The tilt of the floor and the current had made him float toward Larry, and Larry's imagination had done the rest. They lowered the yawl boat and ran the body in to Mona Island, burying it in a shallow grave in one of the caves, for later identification, if possible, by the authorities. Certainly they didn't want it aboard the *Jolly Roger*. This was the first time they had set foot on Mona, but although they had all been eager to explore the island, they were in no mood for it now, and returned quickly to their ship.

The girls had obediently gone below when the corpse was brought aboard. They had seen only a huddled form under canvas, and were only temporarily sobered. Larry and Chris were tired and upset from their ugly task, and when the girls demanded to be allowed to dive, they were in no case to argue. It was still early, and Mr. Currier, secretly wanting to shake the boys out of their depression, seconded the girls.

The anchors were buoyed and the *Jolly Roger* moved into shallower water so the girls could make a dive. It was just the right medicine for Larry and Chris, and they shook off their despondency in the fun of getting the girls ready and in giving them instructions. Although both girls were tall, only one diving dress was small enough to fit them, so they had to dive in turn, at sixty feet. Larry went down briefly to be sure they had no trouble. He climaxed his ascent by inflating his dress when he neared the surface, and "blowing out" of the water to impress the girls.

But both Linda and Mona were frankly scornful of the complicated and cumbersome regulation diving dress, used as they were to their light aqua lungs. "Why don't you throw away those heavy, complicated outfits with all those hoses and just use lungs?" Linda demanded. "I've heard of men going down three and four hundred feet with aqua lungs."

"Sure," said Larry, "and some of them died doing it. A commercial diver goes down to work, not to play. The ordinary person can't operate at the extreme limits of anything without hurting himself, or taking too much risk."

"That's right," agreed Chris. "It's like asking why all airplanes don't operate at altitudes of fifteen miles or more, just because one or two planes have gone that high. It's dangerous for anyone but an expert to fool around in a self-contained rig at much over one hundred feet. I've seen skin divers come up bleeding from the nose and mouth and ears, from stretching the capabilities of their equipment. Under one hundred feet, I'd generally use a self-contained rig, but for anything over that depth, I want a regulation diving dress. Maybe I'm old-fashioned, but I think I'll live longer that way."

Both of the girls wanted to dive to the wrecked ship, but Chris wouldn't permit it on grounds that it was too late in the day. He could see that he was eventually going to have to allow the girls to make at least one visit to the wreck or have no peace, but he didn't feel easy about it. Besides, it really was too late to do it then.

The weather held fine, and they went down to the wreck again soon after sunrise. Chris made the first dive, and located the purser's office and the huge steel door to the strongroom. It would take explosives to open that door. Larry insisted on going down to see it for himself, though there was really no need. As he came back on the deck of the sunken ship, Peter told him on the phone, "Stand by. You've got company."

Then another diver appeared, moving inexpertly over the cluttered deck. Larry advanced and peered into the faceplate. Linda Currier's pretty face smiled back at him.

"Where do you want to go?" he hollered.

"Show me the dead man's stateroom, and the treasure room," she demanded.

Although Larry was hesitant about bringing Linda inside the vessel, he and Chris had already cleared away most of the hazardous wreckage which might foul their lines, burning some of it free with their cutting torches, which used a mixture of oxygen and hydrogen. He led Linda into the saloon, both their torches beaming brightly. She looked in the tragic stateroom, then pulled at the locked handles of the strongroom.

Larry had a sudden idea. The steward's pantry opening off the main saloon had apparently been tightly sealed, and at one end of it he and Chris had discovered an air pocket. Divers often strike these air pockets on a ship. Air that can't escape to the surface is compressed into a pocket on the high side of any compartment in which it is trapped.

On a recent wreck, in more shallow water, a diver can actually open his faceplate in such a pocket without harm. However, the air in this pocket on the *Dona Isabella* was almost completely void of oxygen. The slow decomposition of organic material in the mud and silt deposited through the years had used it up. One breath of air containing no oxygen causes immediate unconsciousness, and at 200 feet would result in death. But Larry had his oxyhydrogen cutting torch with him, with separate valves for oxygen, hydrogen and compressed air. He turned the oxygen valve and aimed the tool into the air pocket without igniting it, thus revivifying the dead air with life-sustaining oxygen. It was a shameless waste of the gas, of which they had none too much aboard. Because of the depth, they were using oxygen and helium instead of compressed air to breathe on their longer dives, to avoid the nitrogen narcosis which would otherwise affect their clearness of thinking and sureness of action after a long period at such a depth. On shorter dives they used the compressed air. Larry was now so intrigued with his mischievous idea that he didn't even consider the waste of oxygen.

Larry led Linda into the pantry and up the slanting deck until they came to a spot where the water came up only to their corselets. Larry leaned forward until his helmet touched Linda's. "Open my faceplate," he told her. "It's all right."

Linda knew how to do it. She had often helped Larry into and out of his diving dress and helmet. Hesitantly she reached up, and unfastened the faceplate. Then Larry opened hers.

Linda giggled. "Isn't this silly?" she inquired.

"It's going to get sillier yet," whispered Larry. "Have you got lipstick on?"

Linda pursed her mouth. "Of course I have. Can't you see?"

"All right, then," said Larry. "Kiss me."

"Oh, Mr. Cahill," responded Linda. "This is so sudden!"

"No, I really mean it," said Larry. "Kiss me good and hard, so the lipstick will come off all over my face. We'll really give them a shock when we get back on the *Jolly Roger*."

Linda laughed. Obediently, she pressed her lips against Larry's cheeks, stopping between kisses to giggle.

"Now on the lips," commanded Larry. Larry decided this was the cleverest idea he had ever had.

When they got back on deck, the effect on Mr. Currier and Chris and Peter, on Mrs. Cahill, and especially on Mona, was all the two could have desired. "What in the world have you two been doing down there?" Mona demanded. "Chris, they've been spooning. Look at Larry's face! How could they possibly—I mean you said it's 200 feet deep—I mean. . . ."

Peter, looking envious, was equally puzzled. "I know your face was clean when I put your helmet on," he said. "What gives?"

"Met up with a mermaid," answered Larry nonchalantly. Linda was laughing too hard for speech.

"How could a mermaid kiss you through your faceplate?" Mrs. Cahill wanted to know.

"Oh, mermaids have ways," Larry answered airily. "And what ways!"

"Weren't you jealous?" Mona asked Linda. Larry answered for her.

"Jealous? I'll say she was. Kept looking for a merman. Couldn't find one. Would have taken up with a wahoo if I hadn't stopped her."

Chris was as puzzled as the others until his eye caught the cutting torch. His eyes twinkled with sudden comprehension. "Mona and I will make a proper investigation of this business tomorrow, won't we, Mona?"

"By golly," said Mr. Currier, "if you and Mona go down together tomorrow, either Mrs. Cahill or I will have to go down to chaperone you."

CHAPTER 22

~~~~~~

Chris was worried that the
Wrangler might appear and interfere with their salvage
efforts, yet he was also eager to work Larry's air pocket
stunt with Mona. Common sense told him that he
shouldn't waste the time, and that it was dangerous to take
the inexperienced girls below to such a depth. Yet he
knew that now Linda had made a dive, he couldn't refuse
Mona.

He compromised by going down with Mona early
the following morning, intending to send her up alone
and remain on the bottom himself to work. They found
the air pocket, and Chris had his tender reward. But when
he led Mona back to the descending line, he couldn't bear
to leave her alone for the slow, tedious ascent.

As Chris and Mona neared the surface, going up in
twenty-five foot stages with long pauses between to decompress, Larry passed them on his way down to see if
a light explosive charge would blast open the door to the
strongroom. They were afraid to use a heavy charge, as
it might scatter any objects that might be in the strong-

room. If there was gold bullion there, they'd never be able to get it out through the door and the long winding corridors of the cabin to the deck where it could be hoisted.

Their plan was to use an oxy-hydrogen cutting torch to burn through the deck above the strongroom, then lower a grab bucket from the *Jolly Roger* right into the strongroom, and bite up and hoist away anything that was in there. It is not desirable for a diver to work close to a grab, because of the danger of fouling his lines or of having something fall on him. Thus, it would facilitate the operation tremendously if they could open the door.

Larry placed the explosive charges, then moved back through the corridors, across the deck to his descending line, and began his ascent. The diver must be clear of the water before an explosive charge is set off, or he will be crushed by the shock wave of the explosion.

When Larry finally regained the deck of the *Jolly Roger*, the charge was set off. They all lined the rail, but the disturbance of the water was slight, since the charge was inside the *Dona Isabella*, and was too light to break through the superstructure. The water surged up in a sudden boil, then subsided. A few bits of wreckage and several dead fish appeared.

Chris and Larry discussed whether they should break their own rule against making two dives in the same twenty-four hour period. Because of their concern about time, Chris finally went down again, after waiting long enough for the water to clear slightly.

Chris telephoned the bad news as soon as he got to the strongroom. Their charge had made hardly any impression on the door, doing little more than bulge some of the plates.

They sat on the *Jolly Roger's* deck, with the hot afternoon sun turning the awning above them golden and translucent, and considered the problem. Should they burn through the *Dona Isabella's* deck with cutting torches, or try to blast a hole? Mr. Currier suggested using a torch to burn the strongroom door open, but Larry explained the great danger, when using a torch inside a wreck, of having escaping gases from the torch trapped below. These gases are highly explosive, and they'd first have to blow or otherwise open up any area where torches were being used to allow the gases to rise to the surface and escape in open air. On the other hand, a good explosives man can cut steel like butter, though there is always danger of damaging or scattering the objects to be salvaged, and steel plates torn by TNT are extremely hazardous to work around.

The feeling of urgency which was spreading aboard the *Jolly Roger* was justified the following morning. As Larry was about to descend with the cutting torch, the black hull of the *Wrangler* appeared on the horizon. There was no point to stopping now, so Larry went down anyway.

This was not going to be easy. Since cutting is essentially a melting operation, there has to be space for the melted slag to run out. Generally the diver cuts at a low spot and works upward, letting the melted steel run down. But at the spot which they had located and marked as being directly over the strongroom, the deck of the *Dona Isabella* was at only a slight angle from the horizontal.

The cutting torch is provided with an air sheath, through which high-pressure air bleeds out and forms an air bubble known as an "artificial atmosphere." It is inside this air bubble that the flame of the cutting tip burns.

Larry got in position, tested the valves of the three gases (compressed air, hydrogen, and oxygen) and telephoned Peter to switch on the igniter. Then he touched the igniter to the torch, and a bluish-green flame flared through the water. He drew the torch slowly over the deck plate, to make a clean, continuous cut. Normally this is a fairly rapid operation, but the level cuts kept clogging with melted metal which hardened as soon as the flame was withdrawn. He had trouble adjusting the flame to maximum cutting efficiency, and his torch frequently went out. Oxy-hydrogen cutting is trickier and requires more experience than some of the other types, but it is best suited to use at great depths.

Larry kept at his task till his allotted two hours on the bottom were up. Then he turned off the torch and left it on the deck for Chris, being particularly careful not to foul its lines as he worked back to his descending line for the hour and a half trip up. Chris passed him, going down to pick up the job where Larry had left off.

In his concentration on his job, Larry had forgotten about the *Wrangler*. As he stopped at the various stages to decompress on the way up, he began to wonder what the *Wrangler's* crew was up to. It was an uncomfortable feeling to have both Chris and himself overside, with no one on the *Jolly Roger* but Mr. Currier, Peter, his mother and the two girls, and with enemies in the vicinity. Perhaps either he or Chris should stay topside as long as the *Wrangler* was around, even though it would slow them up.

By the time he had reached the surface, Larry had fretted himself into quite a stew. As soon as his helmet was removed, he looked around for the *Wrangler*. She was standing well off, near tiny Monita Island northeast of Mona. The others told him that she had cruised close by once, her crew watching the *Jolly Roger* and the waters over the wreck through binoculars, and then had drawn off a couple of miles and stayed there all day.

"They know what we're doing, of course," said Peter. "They were close enough to see the bubbles from the cutting torch come up and break and release smoke."

Chris came up, discouraged at the slow progress they were making with the torches. The strongroom was lined with steel plates below the deck beams as well as above. He thought they had better use explosives. Larry was in favor of going on with the torches. Mr. Currier was asked for an opinion, but refused to give one. He had a deep theoretical knowledge of diving, as of so many other things, and he enjoyed spreading that knowledge. But he never pretended to know something when he did not, and in this question of practical salvage technique, he refused to arbitrate. In the end, they decided to blow in the deck, as the fastest method.

The hovering presence of the *Wrangler* disturbed the idyllic existence they had enjoyed on the *Jolly Roger* until now. They were all worried, and none of them slept well. During the night, Larry, lying sleepless on the cargo hatch where the men were sleeping for the sake of coolness, heard Chris stir restlessly. He whispered to him: "Chris, do you suppose we should get the guns out and load them, in case those guys on the *Wrangler* should try to board us?" They had quite an arsenal in the *Jolly Roger's* arms chests, since none of the Cahill boys had wanted to give up his personal rifle and shotgun.

Chris thought a moment, then said: "No. They've probably got guns aboard too. If we bring out ours, they'll bring out theirs. Someone will get rattled or get an itching trigger finger, and then we'll really have trouble. They may try to hi-jack anything we bring up, but I doubt if they'd kill any of us if we don't start the shooting."

"Funny the way they just hang around," said Larry, "not doing any diving or anything else."

"We'll hear from them when and if we start hoisting anything up from the bottom," said Chris. "Of course, we still don't know if there'll be anything to hoist. My idea is that we'll blow in the deck, take a look in the strongroom to see what's there, but not try to use the grab-bucket now, because the signal for them to move in will be our actually taking something aboard from the *Dona Isabella*. Instead, Peter can run our yawl boat over to Mayaguez, telephone Chief Maddox, and ask him to send a Coast Guard Patrol boat by. The *Wrangler* won't start anything with the Coast Guard around. Maddox can't keep a cutter cruising around here indefinitely. He's only a Chief Boatswain's Mate, not the Commanding Officer of the District. That's why I don't want to call on him till we need him. Of course, we could make a clean breast of the whole business to the Insular authorities on Puerto Rico, and establish a legal claim to whatever we salvage; maybe get police protection too."

"Let's leave that till last," said Larry.

They were in an awkward legal position with the authorities, as are most treasure seekers. The ship had been Spanish. The money in her strongroom, if there was any, came from Cuba, which was a colony of Spain at the time the vessel sank, but was now an independent country. The wreck was on the Santo Domingo side of the Mona Passage, although Mona Island itself belonged to Puerto Rico and therefore to the United States. Let word get out that the Cahills had found treasure, and there might be gunboats from three different countries to claim the right to physical possession of the treasure until the legal tangle was straightened out.

If the crew of the *Wrangler* should get hold of it, they could be expected to cut and run, as they did not have the look of quiet taxpayers. The Cahills intended to declare the treasure, if and when it was recovered, and to file legal claims. But if word got out ahead of time, there could be conflicting national claims, plus claims of the heirs of passengers lost on the *Dona Isabella*, plus the probability of additional competitive treasure seekers. It would be best to keep quiet before taking legal action until the bullion was safe on American soil.

They awoke next morning to find the *Jolly Roger* wallowing in heavy swells from the Northeast. There was no sign of the *Wrangler*, but it was too rough to dive from a boat as small as the *Jolly Roger*, and Max Gsovski, on the *Wrangler*, would know that too. They fully expected to see their tormentors reappear when the water quieted.

A rough sea makes for hazardous diving. If the diver and topside man keep the lines normally taut, the diver can be lifted and then knocked down by the rise and fall of the vessel from which he is diving. If the lines are allowed to go slack, an important safety factor is lost. The topside man can't sense what the diver is doing, can't hold him if he tumbles, can't receive hand signals.

Mona Passage always had a strong current. Now, with choppy seas running across the swells, the *Jolly Roger* was bobbing around in a way that caused Mrs. Cahill to lose her appetite, and the two girls to be abnormally quiet. Linda asked her father why there seemed to be two sets of waves, each running in different directions.

"All waves are caused by the wind, of course," explained Mr. Currier. "While they remain in the area of the wind that produces them, so that they are steady and growing in size, they are called 'seas.' But when they run out from the area, or the wind has dropped and is no longer supplying energy to that particular series of waves, they are known as 'swells.' In the ocean, both seas and swells usually exist in any one place. The 'sea' runs in the direction of the wind prevailing at the time, but the swell may come from anywhere, or from several directions at once. That's why the water looks so confused here."

By mid-afternoon, the water had quieted somewhat, though it was still a little rough for diving. With the *Wrangler* absent, Chris and Larry decided that this was their chance to place the explosives and blow open the deck without the crew of the *Wrangler* knowing about it. The size of the charge had to be carefully calculated. Since the pressure is so much greater on all sides than in the open air, the work to be performed by the explosive is increased, which means closer spacing and higher loading factors. Great force would be required to blow the deck open, but too heavy a blast would scatter the treasure. If there was gold inside, its weight plus the force of the blast might cause the thin lower deck to give way, scattering the treasure hopelessly throughout the hull.

A twenty pound charge of gelignite was decided on. Chris descended and placed the explosive, while Larry stayed topside and kept an eye peeled for the *Wrangler*. She did not appear. The sun was setting in a glorious blaze of color that was reflected clear around the horizon when Chris surfaced. In the brief twilight of the tropics, with everyone aboard holding fingers crossed for luck, they set off the charge.

The *Jolly Roger* lurched and trembled as a boiling surge of water rose above the surface, then subsided in foam. As they watched the bits of wreckage and the swollen bodies of fish killed by the explosion, the running and range lights of a boat appeared from behind Monita Island, where the *Wrangler* had been lurking. With powerful twin engines wide open, the *Wrangler* raced toward them.

"She's fast enough, anyway," remarked Larry.

Chris nodded. "She was probably a World War II Air Force crash boat," he said.

The *Wrangler* came almost alongside, flashing her searchlight over the *Jolly Roger* and the surrounding water. Seeing no further evidence of activity aboard the *Jolly Roger*, the *Wrangler* withdrew a short distance. At irregular intervals all through the night, she would stab at the *Jolly Roger* with her searchlight, apparently anxious to see if any more diving was to be done.

"Let them stay awake if they want," said Chris. "I'm going to sleep." He stretched out on his mattress atop the cargo hatch, and the others did the same. Sleep did not come easily.

CHAPTER 23

~~~~~~

They woke to a calm sea and an empty horizon. Where was the *Wrangler?* Why had she hung around most of the night, then disappeared before daylight? Had she really gone off, or was she hiding behind Monita Island?

"There's no use speculating about those fellows," said Chris. "I still don't think they'll make a move till we actually salvage something, and they'll be around watching to see when we start. We'll fool them by not using any of the lifting tackle till we can get word to Chief Maddox."

"All I want to do right now," said Larry, spreading out his diving dress, "is to get inside the *Dona Isabella* and see what we've got, and I'm going to take a sack down with me to hold some samples of the gold. Chris can wait for the grab bucket if he wants. I want to dip my hands into a treasure chest."

Chris was outwardly calm, but inside he was as eager as Larry to inspect the strongroom and see if the explosives had worked properly; if it had blown a clear en-

167

trance into the room without scattering the contents. After a quick inspection, he wanted to get back aboard the *Jolly Roger* and send Peter off for the Coast Guard. Both divers therefore hurried their preparations, and they descended together, landing on the boat deck of the *Dona Isabella.*

Cautiously they worked their way up to the scene of the explosion. There was a mass of twisted rails, ventilators and other light deck structures, but the main deck plates were still intact. They had bulged slightly from the explosion, but the Cahills were almost as far from gaining entrance to the strongroom as ever. Larry groaned in dejection, while Chris crouched to examine the deck plates minutely. He couldn't understand why they had not been torn apart. The explosive charge had been adequate, and had been properly placed in accordance with the most up-to-date procedure for blasting a steel structure.

Peter was querying Larry over the phone, and Mr. Currier was as eagerly asking Chris for a report. "No luck," was the discouraging message they sent back. Larry and Chris tipped their helmets together for a brief conversation, then decided to make their ascent. Peter called Larry again. "The *Wrangler's* back on the scene again," he said. A little later, as Larry was on the way up, Peter reported again, "The *Wrangler's* really coming up close this time, for a good look at what's going on."

Chris and Larry had been on the bottom only a short time, which speeded up their ascent. They were both disappointed but not discouraged, already thinking of new blasting techniques, and both trying to suppress their worries about the people topside, and what the *Wrangler* was doing. Peter kept chatting with Larry for a time, as was his practice. Then the phone was silent for so long that Larry wondered what was happening. He buzzed

Peter several times, and finally got an answer. "What's up?" asked Larry. "I missed your melodic voice."

"I just had something to take care of," said Peter. "Nothing serious. How about coming up another notch?" Larry felt himself rising another twenty-five feet.

The slow ascent was finally completed. Larry and Chris were helped aboard the *Jolly Roger* and led to the hatch cover to sit. Their helmets were unlocked and lifted off. Larry turned his head, and looked into the face of Max Gsovski.

His blood went to the boiling point in an instant, and he rose in his clumsy diving dress. "What are you doing aboard here?" he shouted at Gsovski.

"Easy, Cahill," said Gsovski confidently. "Just take it easy and no one will get hurt."

Larry looked around him. Gsovski, balancing a heavy wooden cudgel in both hands, was standing close to a pale but angry Peter. Chips, their ex-carpenter, hovered near Mr. Currier, his huge hands open as if he were eager to throttle him. Leaning against the starboard rail were Smitty, Benjamin, and the same sinister man he and Mr. Currier had talked to in Florida, after they had lost the barge-load of cannon. The *Wrangler* was made fast alongside.

"This is piracy, you know," said Chris calmly, as he dropped his weights and started to loosen his corselet.

The *Wrangler's* Captain advanced a step. "Leave that diving dress on, you. This isn't piracy at all. I staked out this wreck long ago. Had it buoyed. You guys are just trying to crowd me out. Well, it won't work. You can take this old scow of yours and clear out."

It wasn't entirely unexpected. Salvage men pull no punches when they're fighting for the same ship. The Captain turned to Gsovski: "Get back aboard the *Wrangler* and get into your diving dress," he told him. "We can handle this crew with these two big guys still in their strait jackets."

Larry felt waves of hot rage sweep up inside him, but he was helpless to resist while still laced and bolted inside the cumbersome diving dress.

"Here you, Smitty," continued the Captain, "you go with Gsovski and help him." Smitty started to say something, but the Captain roared, "Shut up and get going," giving Smitty a shove that was half a blow.

Smitty staggered with the force of the shove, striking his funny bone a sharp blow against a stanchion. His face twisted in pain and anger, Smitty snarled at his Captain, "Don't shove me," and aimed a kick at the Captain's shins. The Captain shifted his weight like a professional fighter and drove a hard fist to the point of Smitty's jaw. The blow fairly lifted Smitty's light weight off the deck, and he collapsed in a huddled heap, out cold.

Chris' eye was roving in search of a weapon, and Larry, Peter and Mr. Currier all moved forward, fists clenched.

"Stand where you are," shouted the Captain, pulling his coat aside. The wicked butt of an automatic pistol showed in a shoulder holster. There was no doubt from the sharpness of the Captain's voice, and the grim reckless look on his hard face, that he meant to carry this business to a finish.

"You, Benjamin," he snarled. "Knock the shackles out of those anchors—bow and stern." Benjamin moved off obediently.

"You're going to have some explaining to do to the Coast Guard and the authorities ashore, Mister," Chris told him grimly.

"Explanations? Ha!" The Captain was amused. "I know what you've been up to, and I know you've kept your mouth shut. There's probably not a soul in the world outside of us on these two ships who knows you've been after treasure. Your word is no better than mine. I was here first. The *Wrangler* was tied up in San Juan before you passed Cuba. You can't go yelling 'Cops' now!" He turned to Benjamin. "All ready?"

They heard the sharp clang of a hammer as Benjamin knocked the shackles loose, and returned. The two boats, locked together, began to swing with the current. "Now the engine," the Captain said to Chips, who grunted and made for the companionway.

Mrs. Cahill and the two Currier girls were down there. As Chris and Larry started forward again, the *Wrangler's* Captain said, "He won't touch the women."

"He'd better not," said Chris.

Larry was beyond words, his mind racing with desperate ideas for recapturing the ship, all of them impractical. There was a succession of heavy blows from the engine room, and Chris winced as he imagined Chips running amok in there, ruining the engine. But worse was to come. Chips reappeared, sweating and looking pleased with himself. He and Benjamin then drew sheath knives and raced around the *Jolly Roger,* cutting the lanyards on the schooner's shrouds and stays, which were set up in the old-fashioned way, with deadeyes; then slashing halyards, topping lifts, sheets, every line used to hoist or handle the sails.

When they were done, the Captain remarked to Chris, "Bon voyage. This current'll take you clear of Cape Rojo. You don't have to worry about grounding. By the time you get rigged up again and get to shore, we'll be on our way with the treasure, if there's any in that wreck below. And thanks for opening her up for us. We were just waiting for you to blast her."

The Captain, Chips and Benjamin scrambled over the rail on to the *Wrangler* and prepared to cast off.

They paid no attention to Smitty, who still lay unconscious on the deck. "Here, take your playmate with you," Chris called, pointing at Smitty's crumbled form. The *Wrangler's* Captain shook his head. "Keep him," he said. "We don't need him, and I'm fed up with his whining and fawning and then turning all of a sudden to bite like a rat."

The *Wrangler's* engines started up, and she moved slowly to the spot where the *Jolly Roger* had been moored, dropping anchors fore and aft. The *Jolly Roger* continued to drift down the Mona Passage while her stunned crew looked at one another.

Linda Currier's clear, unfrightened voice came from the cabin. "Can you untie us now?" she called. Peter came to with a start, and he and Mr. Currier raced for the companionway. Larry and Chris looked at one another in fresh rage. They hadn't realized the women had been tied.

Mona, Linda and Mrs. Cahill came out on deck rubbing their wrists. They had been caught by Benjamin as they were hauling guns and ammunition out of the arms chest, and tied up with strong line and tight knots. Swiftly, Larry and Chris told them all that had happened. Linda turned to Larry and wailed, "All that lovely treasure, ready and waiting for them. And after all your work!"

Suddenly Larry remembered something, and began to laugh. The humor of the situation grew on him, till he became almost hysterical and had to sit on the hatch cover, still in his diving dress. The others clamored to know what was so funny, pushing at him when he didn't answer—he couldn't. Finally Chris' pushes got so hard Larry couldn't ignore them any more. He wiped the tears from his eyes, swallowed a little of his laughter, and explained: "Those guys think all they have to do is to send Max down to guide a bucket, and he can scoop up gold and silver coins and fill the bucket for them. Instead, they're going to find a still solid ship . . . in fact, the most solid ship I ever heard of. Our blast should have punched a big hole in the deck, but all it did was to bulge a few plates. It's not going to be as easy as they think. They may not even have explosives aboard."

"They haven't," came a strange voice from the scuppers. Everyone whirled. It was Smitty, whom they had all forgotten. He had come to his senses and was sitting there, quietly taking in the conversation. Now he rose to his feet, gingerly touched his swollen jaw, and moved over to the group on deck. He addressed himself to Chris. "I suppose you'll want to ask me some questions." It was a statement, not an inquiry. Smitty was a miserable looking specimen as he stood there, a three-day growth of beard on his thin lined face, his small body wriggling nervously, his clothes dirty and disreputable.

Chris had long since learned that silence is an effective questioner. He sat on the hatch while Mona and Mr. Currier helped him out of his diving dress, and nodded for Smitty to continue. That individual unexpectedly turned almost defiant. "All right," he said, "so we did hear you talking about the *Dona Isabella* and that frigate in Florida. We didn't intend to listen. But any man spreads his ears when he hears the word 'treasure.' You had no more right to that treasure than I did. No one has a right to treasure but the man who gets there first. You just happened to learn about the *Dona Isabella*. I just happened to learn about it too—from you. I always had a notion you'd go treasure hunting. That's why I tried to be friends when I was working for you. But you didn't want to be friends with me. No one ever does."

Smitty paused as if for questions, then went on again. "I had as much right to the treasure as anyone. I couldn't get shares with you, so me and the other two found someone else to play with. Yes," turning to Mr. Currier, "we salvaged your cannon, too. And we had a right to it. Sold the whole load for six thousand dollars, and you know what my share was?" he looked around the fascinated group, as if expecting them to guess. Linda and Larry shook their heads. "Five hundred measly dollars," said Smitty disgustedly. He looked back at where the *Wrangler* was moored, and spat contemptuously on the deck. Chris came to life.

"Wipe that up!" he roared. Smitty grimaced apologetically; went to his knees and wiped up the spittle with his shirt sleeve, then rose again. He was still not abashed.

Smitty continued, speaking calmly. "We've been waiting for you to show up and go to work on the wreck. That Gsovski, he's no great shakes of a diver. They're all a bunch of dopes, that lot, except the Captain. I'd have got their money too, before I was done with 'em, the Captain's too, tough as he is. That ain't the first time he's hit me. I've got a knife that's been itching for his blood.

"Sure, I wanted to get rich. I've been rich before, lots of times. It was easier for me to get money than to keep it, and I never got but ten cents on the dollar when I spent it. But I've had money, and I'd like to have it once more before I die—I like the feel of it. Well, that's done. You're stuck with me, and I'm stuck with you. Treat me right, and I'll work for you, help you get this hooker back in shape, even help you go after the treasure again if you're game. They ain't got a pound of powder aboard the *Wrangler* and they haven't got a cutting torch that'll work in that depth of water, either. Oxy-acetylene, that's what they got—no good except in shallow water. They were depending on you fellows to do the job for them. If your blast didn't open up the *Dona Isabella* like you say, they're stuck too."

"What do you think they'll do?" asked Chris.

"Probably hightail it over to Mayaguez or San Juan as fast as they can to get explosives, and try to blow her open before you can get your rigging spliced and sail in to shore," said Smitty. "You ain't licked yet. It'll take 'em a while to buy explosives. You can't pick them up just anywhere. I'll bet they have to go to San Juan to get them—the Captain has friends there. Even when he gets explosives, he probably won't be able to blast a hole, any more than you were."

"What do you know about blasting?" demanded Chris.

"I know what I know," said Smitty insolently. "Are we gonna stand here all day, or are we gonna splice the rigging and go after that treasure ourselves?"

Chris, now out of the diving dress, stepped over to Smitty, grabbed his shirt front in one hand, and pulled him close. "Don't get insolent with me, or with any of us." Chris told him quietly. "We'll let you tag along with us for now, but strictly on good behavior. And this is *our* treasure, not yours. Don't forget that."

Smitty was not quelled, but his insolence subsided. "I just want to help, and I got an idea I can be more help than you think. I'll leave you to judge whether I'm entitled to any part of the treasure. That's fair enough, isn't it?"

Chris stepped back. "All right," he said. "But don't be too sure there *is* a treasure. We're all acting as if we knew for certain that the strongroom is full of gold. More likely it's got an old safe in it with a few jewels and a little paper money that's nothing but pulp now."

"There's gold on the *Dona Isabella*," said Smitty confidently.

By this time the current had carried them past Punta de Oesta on Mona Island, and the *Wrangler* was out of sight. "I wish we could get in to shore close enough to anchor," said Chris. "Then we wouldn't be carried so far away. And I'd hate to run into bad weather while we're helpless like this."

"Why don't you tow the *Jolly Roger* in with the yawl boat?" asked Linda. Chris looked at her and then at Larry. They had forgotten the sixteen foot open boat the *Jolly Roger* carried on davits across her stern. The *Wrangler's* crew had forgotten it, too. The boat had a ten horse power, heavy duty engine in it, and could either tow or push the *Jolly Roger* as long as the water stayed calm.

They lowered the yawl boat. Larry took a line from the *Jolly Roger*, and slowly towed her in toward the island. The water in the passage and around Mona Island is very deep, and they had to run up almost to the cliffs of the island itself before it was shallow enough for them to anchor. Their two big anchors had been lost when Benjamin knocked the shackles loose, and they had only the light bower anchor left, and not much cable. It would be an insecure anchorage if the wind shifted to any other quarter, but as long as the Northeast trades continued to blow, they were in shelter.

All hands except Chris immediately turned to the rigging, reeving new lines where strength was needed, and putting long splices in the halyards, which were cut low enough so that no strain would be put on the splice when the sails were up. Smitty did more work than any of them, his nimble fingers unlaying and laying the lines at twice Larry's best speed. Mrs. Cahill and the girls brought out canvas, palms and needles to patch the sails where they had been slashed, while Chris tackled the discouraging job of turning the engine back from junk to the piece of efficient machinery it had been. Fortunately, it was a diesel, very heavily built, with fewer exposed parts which could be smashed than a gasoline engine has. They had a fair supply of spare parts aboard. Chris thought the case was not hopeless.

They worked the rest of that day, part of the night, and started early the following morning. The work went faster than they had expected, and faster, certainly, than the *Wrangler's* crew might have imagined. Larry wanted to sneak around the point in the yawl boat for a quick look at the *Wrangler*, to see if she was still over the wreck. Chris forbade this, however, as too risky. If the *Wrangler's* Captain suspected they were so close, and that they were repairing the damage so quickly, he might pay them another visit, though the story would be different this time if he did, with Chris and Larry on board and in shape to resist.

Repair of the rigging went faster than repairs to the engine. On the second evening after they had been set adrift, a council of war was held on the *Jolly Roger's* cargo hatch, with Smitty on the edge of the group. The question was: Should they stay where they were, while one of them took the yawl boat over to Mayaguez and telephoned to Chief Maddox for help? Or should they all sail over in the *Jolly Roger?* Smitty's eyes opened wide when he realized that the Cahills already had ties with the Coast Guard.

The question was answered by the weather. The trade winds had been unseasonably mild. Now the wind was piping up, and working around toward the North. Their anchorage was not too secure, especially with only a light anchor down, and with a lee shore so close. The *Jolly Roger* would have to move, and anyway it was becoming too rough for the small yawl boat to risk the trip to Mayaguez.

Meanwhile, they had no idea what was happening over at the wreck of the *Dona Isabella.* "Why don't I take some food and a rifle, and stay on Mona Island while the rest of you go over to Mayaguez?" suggested Larry. "I can keep an eye on the *Wrangler*, and you can pick me up when you return."

"What good would it do to 'keep an eye on the *Wrangler*,' as you put it?" asked Mrs. Cahill. "You can't do anything about them, and you might get in trouble if they should come ashore."

"Oh, I could hide easily enough if I had to, couldn't I, Mr. Currier?" said Larry.

"Yes," agreed Mr. Currier. "I don't believe there's a better island in the world to hide on than Mona, with all its caves. But I don't see what good it would do to watch the *Wrangler*, Larry."

"It could do this much good," argued Larry, who was intrigued by the idea of a night alone on the island. "We've all agreed they'll have to leave the wreck to get explosives, if they're going to do any good. Now, when the Coast Guard comes by, anyone who has a buoy on that wreck has a prior claim for salvage, hasn't he?"

"Yes, that's right," agreed Chris and Mr. Currier, both of them now deeply interested.

"The Coast Guard has no official notice that we had a buoy on it first," continued Larry. "Even Chief Maddox only has Chris' word for it. He hasn't actually *seen* the buoy, or our boat, or any of us standing by the buoy. On the other hand, if the Coast Guard finds the *Wrangler* sitting over the wreck with a buoy down and diving operations underway, it'll be hard for them to drive them off, won't it? The *Wrangler's* bunch will claim that they've been there all along, that we've never been there. Seems to me that Chief Maddox can get his hands all tied up with red tape, no matter how his sympathies may lie."

"The Chief has quite a way of handling red tape," Chris smiled. "But go on, Larry, you're making sense."

"My idea," said Larry, "is that you leave me the yawl boat. I'll anchor it where it can't be seen from the wreck, yet close enough so I can get out or back in a hurry. Then I'll keep watch. If I see the Coast Guard boat coming, I'll go out. If the *Wrangler* isn't back yet, then there I am on our buoy that we put down to the wreck. If the *Wrangler* is already there, then I'll wait till the Coast Guard is close enough to protect me, but when they get to the scene of the wreck, they'll find both me *and* the *Wrangler* claiming the buoy. At least we'll have a better claim than if only the *Wrangler* is there."

"I don't like this," said Mrs. Cahill, "that's a bad lot on that other boat. Larry could get hurt."

"If Larry will give us his solemn promise not to do anything reckless, to do just what he has suggested here, and nothing more, then I think it would be a good move," said Chris.

It was decided to go along with Larry's idea, and since there was no point in risking the *Jolly Roger* any longer than necessary in that exposed spot, they decided to carry out the plan at once. Larry assembled food and water, a compass, binoculars and other equipment, while Chris copied an outline of the island from the chart, and Mr. Currier sketched on this crude map his recollections of the landmarks and paths of the island.

Larry wanted to take his rifle ashore with him. Chris consented reluctantly, and only after repeated warnings to Larry about using or even displaying it. Possession of a weapon in some circumstances can be more hazardous than being unarmed, and Chris thought this was such a case. Yet he knew, too, the comfort and confidence a weapon can give a man alone, and for this reason he finally agreed to let Larry take his Remington along.

Larry got off in the yawl boat, and stood by as the *Jolly Roger* hoisted her sails, got up the anchor, then fell off the wind and filled on her course to Mayaguez. She was an inspiring sight, her white sails reflecting the light from the millions of stars above; bright pin points of phosphorescent light burning briefly in her bow wash and in the water that bubbled up in her wake. Then she dissolved into the velvety night, and Larry was left alone. And very lonesome.

CHAPTER *24*

~~~~~~

Larry's first job was to locate
a spot along the precipitous shores of the island where
the yawl boat would be reasonably secure from the rising
seas, concealed from the site of the wreck of the *Dona
Isabella*, and yet close enough so he could get over to the
wreck in a hurry. He passed the tall cliff with the over-
hanging rock, suggestively called in Spanish "Punto Caigo
o no Caigo"— "Shall I fall or not"— came abreast of Cape
Barrionuevo, was cheered by the light ashore in the cabin
of the Insular Forest Ranger, and then found a cove exactly to his liking.

He beached the boat, unloaded all his equipment except his rifle, then studied the tide marks ashore. The tidal
range in the Antilles is slight. He anchored so that the
boat would be just afloat at low tide, carrying an extra
line ashore to make fast to a boulder. Then he looked up
at the sheer face of the precipice above him. He hadn't
considered the need to climb these volcanic cliffs. His
food and equipment were in an old seabag, and he slung
it knapsack fashion over his shoulder to have both hands

free to climb. A short way down the beach, he located a narrow twisting path leading up the cliff—whether made by animals or human beings he couldn't tell. Fearfully he began to climb.

There were several dangerous turns in the trail, but Larry hugged the side of the cliff and worked his way around. Tired, hot and breathless, he had almost reached the top when he saw the dim opening of a cave. This would do nicely for a hiding place. Larry turned his flashlight into the cave. It was narrow and deep, but the floor was fairly level. He crossed the lip, turned off his flashlight, and looked out to sea. There was nothing in sight but the wide restless waters and the blazing heavens of the tropic night. The trade wind was blowing hard—up to forty knots in the gusts. He couldn't be sure whether or not he could spot the site of the wreck from this perch, so he went on to a higher point.

Narrowing his eyes, he could see the sky glow from the lighthouse on Cape Engano on Hispaniola. With his compass he took a bearing on the light. Northwest by North. According to Larry's roughly sketched map, the site of the wreck and of any salvage operations should be visible either from the top of the cliff or the cave. With his binoculars, he scanned the water in the direction of the wreck. He thought there was a black smudge which might be the *Wrangler*, but couldn't be sure. If it was, they were not showing any lights.

It was chilly in the blast of the wind. Larry took out his blanket, rolled himself in it, and tried to sleep. But his nerves were on edge, and he couldn't get comfortable. Perhaps he'd be better off in the cave. He worked his way down again, shining his flashlight on the precarious trail. It would be better to have the light seen from the *Wrangler* than to tumble to the beach far below. There were tracks on the trail. Larry looked at them closely. They were cloven. Goats, of course.

Larry settled himself at the mouth of the cave. Still he couldn't sleep. He began to meditate on the romantic history of Mona Island, and to wonder what humans before him had spent a night in this cave. Perhaps Christopher Columbus visited it. Columbus had stopped at Mona Island—in fact, while at Mona he had the first attack of the sickness that was to eat away his health and resolution. Captain Jennings had hidden his treasure in a cave like this one—perhaps in this very cave. The swashbuckler Kofresi had come here with the frightened señorita he had abducted from Mayaguez. Even that archetype of piracy, Captain Kidd, had stopped at Mona Island when on his way North for what was to prove his last voyage. Kidd knew he had been proclaimed a pirate when he stopped at Mona. Later, when he paused at Gardiner's Island at the tip of Long Island, Captain Kidd buried treasure a mile from John Gardiner's manor house. This was not Kidd's full treasure, but just a nest-egg which he left in case he should not be able to clear himself with the authorities, and should have to flee. Why wouldn't he have left a similar cache on Mona Island, and for the same reason?

These were fascinating speculations, and this was the perfect place for them, in a dark cave at night, alone on a tropical island. Only the speculations weren't quite so much fun as they should be, because Larry had become conscious of certain faint sounds in the gloom of the cavern behind him. He scorned himself for his traitorous imagination, which conjured up ghosts of Captain Kidd back to reclaim his treasure—or of men murdered or drowned at Mona. Drowned! It wasn't far from here that they had buried the poor soul whose body they had re-

covered from the deck of the *Dona Isabella*. And those
tracks in the path outside. Goats have cloven hoofs. So
does the devil.

Grimly Larry tried to push these childish thoughts
out of his mind. He almost succeeded, when there was a
definite sound behind him. In a cold sweat of terror he
jumped to his feet, thinking fleetingly of his rifle, which
he had left in the launch. A lot of good it would do him
now! He flicked on his flashlight. From the dim gloom of
a deep passageway, a pair of vertical-pupilled eyes glared
at him. They came closer. Larry shoved the light a little
lower. It was an unspeakably evil, devilish face, with a
long beard, and horns above. Then Larry expelled his
breath in a great sigh of relief. It was nothing but one of
the goats with which the island abounded.

Thoroughly ashamed of his terror, he shouted at the
goat, and heard it scamper back out of sight. Then he lay
down on his blanket, and this time managed to fall asleep.

He woke to a blazing morning, and looked out at an
empty sea. A plume of smoke marked a distant steamer,
but there was no sign of the *Wrangler*. Even though the
face of the cliff was in shadow, he could see the openings
of several caves similar to his, some of them close to the
water, others high in the cliffs. After munching a couple
of sandwiches, and taking a cautious drink of water (for
he had to be careful of his stores) Larry went back into
the cave for a closer examination.

It extended far back into the island, with the first passage branching off to numerous smaller ones. Probably
they branched off in turn—it would be easy to get lost in
there. A greenish phosphorescent glow came from the
rocks, and stalagmites and stalactites stood about in eerie
grace. Small lichens grew on some of the rocks, lizards
scampered about, and green moss hung overhead. There

was plenty of evidence of goats, but none that man had ever been there.

Larry settled down to a long wait, scanning the water with his binoculars, munching a bit of food from time to time, occasionally dozing. Just before noon he saw a slim black sliver between two splashes of white. It was the *Wrangler*, throwing up huge bow waves as she raced past Monita Island. She was really making knots! As she approached the site of the wreck, she slowed, her bow dipped, and she came to anchor. With his binoculars, Larry could see a diver in full dress except for his helmet sitting ready on her deckhouse. That would be Gsovski. Larry's fists clenched. How he'd like to wipe the smirk off Gsovski's face with his knuckles! They were losing no time on board the *Wrangler*. A diving stage and a Jacob's ladder were lowered; Gsovski climbed over the side, and one of the others clamped the helmet in place.

Larry speculated on what they were doing. Apparently Gsovski had gone down soon after the *Jolly Roger* had been cast adrift. He chuckled as he thought of the language which must have greeted Gsovski's announcement that the strongroom had *not* been blown open by the Cahills, but was still intact. The *Wrangler* must have sped to San Juan to get explosives, and have just now returned.

There was a bustle of activity on the *Wrangler*. Through the binoculars, Larry could see that they were lowering explosives to Gsovski. It looked like an awful lot of explosives. Larry hoped they didn't split the whole ship open, and scatter the treasure far and wide over the sea bottom. Gsovski must be on the way up now. They'd blow the charge, and then they'd have to wait till morning before it would be safe for Gsovski to go down again. Larry could only hope that a Coast Guard cutter, or the *Jolly Roger*, or both, would be on the scene by then.

Here was Gsovski, coming over the side. A few minutes later, an immense geyser of water rose to the sky. What a charge they must have blown! But what was this? Gsovski was getting ready to go down again. That was dangerous—to make two dives to such a depth in the same day. They probably didn't even have a recompression chamber on board. Gsovski was risking the bends. What's more, the water below would still be clouded by silt and dirt blown up from the bottom.

The *Wrangler* swung her boom over the side, and began lowering a weighted cargo net. Larry waited, chewing his fingernails in impatience and suspense. Then the twin lenses of his binoculars saw the winch operating. The net came up again. Thank heavens, still empty. Despite the size of the blast, that strongroom still must not be open! When Gsovski got back aboard, the *Wrangler* hove her anchors short, and took off again in the direction of Desecheo Island, Borinquen Point, and San Juan.

What were they up to now? Perhaps they had used all the explosives they had been able to get in one big blast. Larry wondered what the *Dona Isabella* was made of, to withstand this repeated heavy blasting. They might have gone back for more explosives, or for a cutting torch. In any case, it behooved Larry to get out over the wreck, and make fast to the marker buoy, to establish their claim in case the Coast Guard came along.

He was no sooner on the spot than he saw pointed sails rising from the west. It must be—yes, it *was* the *Jolly Roger*, coming up under both sail and power at a tremendous clip for such a heavy vessel. Chris was in diving dress, and as soon as the others had hoisted Larry and the yawl boat on the stern davits, Chris was over the side to pick up the two anchor chains which the *Wrangler's* boarding party had knocked loose.

CHAPTER 25

Larry was impatient to hear the news from the *Jolly Roger*. They had reached Mayaguez without incident, and had telephoned Chief Maddox at Coast Guard headquarters in San Juan. Unfortunately, one of the two cutters ordinarily stationed there was patrolling the waters off Culebra Island, to keep small boats clear of the Air Force bombing range. The other had gone to the assistance of a small yacht, and was towing her in to Ensenada Honda, between Puerto Rico and the Virgin Islands. This boat was then going to circumnavigate Puerto Rico, stopping briefly at Ponce. Maddox promised to radio the cutter to look in at operations around Mona, and said that he'd try to get a pass so he could board the cutter himself at Ponce.

Chris took time while he was below to make a brief inspection of the *Dona Isabella*, after he had recovered the *Jolly Roger's* anchor chains. He reported that the *Isabella's* decks were a terrible mess, strewn with wreckage, and that the funnel would probably topple if a blast as big as

187

the last one was repeated. But though the deck over the strongroom was badly bulged, it was still intact.

Smitty had been listening to this discussion with feverish interest. "How are you making your inserts?" he asked. Chris turned to him in surprise.

"Do you know anything about explosives?" he demanded.

"I know everything about 'em," grinned Smitty.

"All right, then," said Larry. "Suppose you tell us what's holding that ship together?"

"You're going at it the wrong way. The *Dona Isabella* won't break up like a ship of American or British steel. She's like a soft pete. You got to know how to handle your soup and your mud."

"Soft pete. Soup. Mud. What are you talking about, Smitty?" wondered Larry. Smitty looked over his shoulder and around the deck. "I'll tell you if you'll swear to keep it secret," he said. They all agreed, and Smitty continued. "A 'soft pete' is a nickname for an old-fashioned safe, made to resist fire more than safe-cracking. They're made of soft iron instead of case-hardened steel, and they've got to be handled different."

They understood now. The term "soup" was underworld slang for nitroglycerine. Smitty was, or had been, a safe-cracker. They listened intently, half amused, half shocked at this revelation. Smitty went on: "You're not blasting modern steel plates, which are hard but brittle. The *Dona Isabella* is built of old, soft Swedish iron, not steel at all. She'll bend, but she won't snap . . . not unless you handle her right."

Mr. Currier interrupted. "Smitty is right. The *Dona Isabella* was built in Sweden, and practically all of the ships built in the 1870's, when her keel was laid, were built of iron."

Smitty nodded complacently. "You've probably been

using the most up-to-date methods, which are designed for modern steel plate. Now, here's what you've got to do to open up that ship like she was a sardine can."

He went on to explain the technique of making the inserts and of packing the explosive to direct the force of the blast in the desired direction. Larry and Chris sketched out the location and nature of the spot they wanted to blast open, and Smitty showed them exactly how to proceed.

"Why don't you come down yourself and help us place the charge?" Chris asked Smitty.

Smitty shook his head emphatically. "Not me! You'll never get me down there with all them sharks and octopuses and things. I'm a dry land man, I am. I don't even like boats, though I've spent a lot of years at sea. It makes a good way to lay low after a big job—to go to sea. Police never suspect you if you've got regular seaman's papers. They figure a sailor's too dumb to learn how to crack a safe, and mostly they are, too."

Chris went down early the next morning, and set the charges according to Smitty's specifications. It didn't take him long. The charge was moderate, and the tower of water blown up by the explosion was much smaller than in their previous blasts. This was a good sign. It meant that more of the force was directed downward.

As soon as the water had time to clear, Larry descended to inspect the strongroom. He hadn't stood on the deck of the *Dona Isabella* since before the *Wrangler's* blast. He was amazed at the destruction, and had to move very slowly, with tight air hose and life line, to prevent fouling. When he came to the deck over the strongroom, his heart gave an exultant leap. A four foot hole had been blown right through the deck, its edges jagged with folds of iron plate, all bent down into the strongroom. Jubilantly he reported his findings over the telephone. "That's swell," came back Peter's voice. "But you'd better ascend now. The *Wrangler's* coming back."

"Come up nothing!" said Larry excitedly. "Are you crazy? It'll only take me a couple of minutes to find out whether or not we've hit treasure. I'm going in."

Cautiously Larry felt his way through the hole in the deck, lowering himself feet first, and keeping his lines as clear as possible. He called for more line, and was almost on the bottom when Chris' voice instead of Peter's came over the telephone. "Larry, you come out of that right away," he ordered. "The *Wrangler's* almost on us, and there's no telling what they'll do with you helpless down there. I'm going to bring you up fast and then clap you in the recompression chamber. This is an emergency!"

"Chris, I'm in the strongroom now. Just give me a couple more feet of line," pleaded Larry, unable to think of anything but the possible treasure. "It'll only take me a few seconds to see what's here."

"No!" came Chris' angry voice. "You'll get no more line. If you weren't in that hole with all that wreckage, I'd haul you up whether you liked it or not. Come out!"

But Larry, sniffing treasure, was beyond reason. He was carrying one turn of the air hose and life line over his arm, so that a sudden surge of tide or surface wave action wouldn't cause him to lose his balance. Now he shook off this coil, flicked on his light, and looked around him.

The strongroom was almost empty except for a huge, old-fashioned safe, and four small metal boxes about two feet square and three feet long. He tried to lift one of the boxes, but it was as immovable as if it were welded to the deck. He attacked it with a pinch bar from his sack of tools, but couldn't even begin to make an impression on it. With such a weight, and in boxes that strong and that thoroughly locked and bolted, there *must* be gold inside.

All this time, Chris' voice was droning in his ear alternately commanding and pleading for him to come up. Suddenly Larry came to his senses. He must be causing them terrible anguish on the *Jolly Roger*—and he was in no comfortable situation himself. He certainly didn't want to regain the *Jolly Roger*, have his helmet removed, and look into the sneering face of Max Gsovski as he had on his last dive. Cautiously he inflated his suit enough to float up through the opening in the deck, feeling his way around the torn plates, and telling Chris to keep his lines taut. He moved over to his descending line, and told Chris he was ready to start his ascent.

"What's the *Wrangler* doing now?" he asked Chris. "Nothing," was the answer. "Just drifting around. They seem to be discussing or arguing about something. I've got my rifle out—I'm not going to let them board us while you're down there, even if I have to shoot."

The slow ascent continued, with the interminable waits to decompress. "Anything new on the *Wrangler?*" Larry asked again. He was answered this time by Peter. "They're up to something. Chris is trying to figure it out through the binoculars. They're rigging a long pole at an angle over the bow. Now they've got a grappling iron up forward. I can't figure it."

Larry was lifted again to the next decompression stage. Suddenly he felt a tremendous jerk. He was lifted rapidly about fifty or sixty feet, then dropped back about thirty. Turning his air valves in a frenzy to keep from ballooning to the surface from the change in air pressure, or being squeezed into his helmet, Larry turned sick with fright. He knew something was happening to him. The normal rate of ascent was only twenty-five feet at a time, with pauses between, and Peter would never let him fall like that, with the terrible risk of a squeeze. "What's happening?" he screamed over the phone. Peter's voice came back, and he could tell that Peter was making a supreme effort to keep his poise.

"Larry, you've got to try to keep calm. Here's what happened. They ran the *Wrangler* close alongside us. That long pole they rigged in the bow scooped up your lines, and they've pulled the lines over the bow with the grappling iron. Chips is standing over your lines with an axe, ready to cut them, but Chris has a bead on him with the Remington, and he'll blow Chips' head off if he even starts to swing that axe. The Captain of the *Wrangler* has a gun too . . . a pistol. I don't know what happens now. *Where's* that Coast Guard?"

It was a stalemate, but an ugly one for Larry. He was still sixty feet down. He could inflate his suit and blow out on the surface, but what would happen then? Would Chips or one of the others on the *Wrangler* cut his air line? Or would Peter and the others be able to haul him aboard? Probably not, with his lines caught over the *Wrangler's* bow.

Peter's voice came again. He was talking earnestly, but softly. The *Wrangler* must be pretty close if Peter was afraid they'd overhear him. "Stand by for a rescue, Larry. Linda had a brainstorm. Wait for her."

Wait for her? Larry was baffled. He buzzed his phone again, but Peter did not answer. Then he saw Linda Currier, in face mask, aqua lung and foot flippers, swimming rapidly toward him. She was pulling a long hose and a light line behind her.

Larry understood at once what the plan was. It was to be the Sam Dougherty rescue repeated. He put his hand on his air intake valve and waited. Linda first made the light line fast to him. Then she took the air hose, and gave several tugs. Water began to stream out of the hose as someone on the *Jolly Roger* turned the valve on the air volume tank. Then air streamed through the hose in an explosion of bubbles.

Larry held the hose for Linda, closed his air intake and exhaust valves, and waited while Linda struggled with the coupling of his regular air hose. She got it uncoupled, and coupled on the new air hose. Larry reopened his valves. Water that had entered his line when Linda uncoupled it streamed into his helmet and ran down into his diving dress. Then there was the life-giving rush of air—just in time, for Larry's senses were already beginning to reel from breathing the carbon dioxide of his own exhalations when he had closed the valves, and had only the air trapped in the dress and helmet to breathe.

Linda tugged again on the line, and Larry felt it go taut at the signal, to keep him from dropping when she cut the life line. Then she began sawing away at his life line. It parted, and Larry felt himself swing pendulum-fashion under the *Jolly Roger*, with Linda swimming beside him. He was drawn up a little faster than the regular decompression rate, and broke the surface on the side of the *Jolly Roger* away from the *Wrangler* and the diving stages.

Mr. Currier and Mona were crouched over the rail, concealed by the cabin from those on the *Wrangler*. They had lowered a Jacob's ladder, and had a safety line ready for Larry. His helmet was unlocked and lifted off, Mr. Currier having a hard struggle with it. Larry mounted the ladder and slid prone on the deck behind the cabin. Linda followed him. "Get me out of this dress" whispered Larry. They unlaced his boots and helped him get clear.

Larry crept on hands and knees to the break of the deckhouse and peeked around it. Larry and Peter were standing at the rail, both grimly holding their deer rifles. The *Wrangler* was barely thirty feet away. Larry could see his lines looped over the bow of the *Wrangler*, with

Chips standing over them with an axe on his shoulder. Apparently no one knew quite how to solve the situation. Larry hissed at Chris, "Okay. I'm aboard," and saw both Chris' and Peter's backs stiffen and then relax in relief.

The solution to the still uncomfortable situation appeared around Punta Oesta—a trim gray Coast Guard patrol boat. It opened its throttle at sight of the *Wrangler* and the *Jolly Roger* broadside to broadside.

There was swift reaction on board the *Wrangler*. Larry's lines were dumped overboard, and there was the flash of busy knives as they cut the lashings on the long pole slanting overboard into the water. The Coast Guard boat ran between the *Jolly Roger* and the *Wrangler*. Chief Maddox stepped out of the wheelhouse and hailed: "What's going on here?"

The Captain of the *Wrangler*, an expression of almost comic innocence and righteous indignation on his tough face, answered, "We were working on a salvage job, and this other boat muscled in on us."

Maddox turned toward the *Jolly Roger*. "That right?" he asked, showing no sign of recognition.

"It's exactly wrong," Chris called back. "We were here first, and they crowded in on us. Look, we've got two anchors down, and they've got only one light one. We've got a buoy to the salvage job; they haven't."

"Do either of you want to put in a legal complaint against the other one?" asked Chief Maddox.

There was brief consultation on both the *Wrangler* and the *Jolly Roger*. A formal complaint to the Coast Guard would mean inquiries, possible court action, lawyers. Chris answered, "No. Just keep them off our backs." The Captain of the *Wrangler* also shook his head.

"Stand by, both of you," ordered Maddox. "I'm sending a man aboard to inspect you." The Coast Guard boat eased over to the *Wrangler*, and an armed Coast Guardsman leaped aboard. Then the *Wrangler* swung toward the *Jolly Roger*. Chief Maddox himself clambored over the rail.

"Are you all right?" he asked in a low, urgent tone. Chris nodded. "Only just. We were in a tight spot. Can you drive them away?"

Maddox laughed. "I'll make a show of inspecting your papers and legally required equipment. Joe Soames is on the other boat, and don't worry, Joe will find violations! We'll order them back to San Juan till they've cleared the violations."

Any documented boat has to observe certain strict safety regulations, and Joe Soames didn't have to invent any violations on the *Wrangler*. She was deficient in several respects.

"How about the treasure?" Maddox wanted to know. All hands turned to Larry.

"I think it's there, but I couldn't open the boxes," he said.

Mr. Currier pushed forward. "Were they about two feet square and three feet long?" he asked. Larry nodded. "Were they all-metal, heavily bound on the corners, with double bolts on the front, the top, and each end, and with two ring bolts on each end?" Again Larry nodded. Mr. Currier drew in his breath and let it out in a long sigh. "We've found a treasure, then. Because that's exactly what the Spanish government money chests of that period were like!"

Mona and Linda gave yelps of delight, and hugged Mrs. Cahill, while the three Cahill brothers grinned foolishly at one another. Chief Maddox clapped Chris on the shoulder. "I've got to go now. Better bring the chests to San Juan and turn them over to the Insular Treasury Department or the Bank of Puerto Rico for safekeeping. I'll see you in San Juan."

After the Coast Guard boat and the *Wrangler* had left, Chris and Larry lost no time in stripping the *Jolly Roger's* heavy gaff of the foresail, and rigging it over the side, braced by vanes. Chris gave Larry a terrific tongue-lashing for disobeying topside commands when he was on the bottom and had lost his head in treasure fever. Larry took the tirade with shamefaced patience. He knew he deserved it. But it was hard to accept the punishment. Larry would have to stay on deck while Chris had the honor of fastening the treasure chests to the lifting tackle.

Chris went to the bottom. It took little time for him to attach slings to the four treasure chests, and for the others to hoist them aboard with the power winch. The big safe was a more difficult problem, but Chris managed to work it through the hole in the *Dona Isabella's* deck, and it came aboard too.

They fairly itched to open the chests as they waited during Chris' long ascent. But it wouldn't be fair to open the chests before Chris was on deck to share the thrill. They paced nervously about, never far from the four black, dripping boxes and the huge safe. Smitty in particular was unable to sit still a moment, watching the others suspiciously as if he feared they would throw him overboard.

Finally Chris surfaced. They all gathered around one of the chests. It proved impossible to break it open with ordinary tools, so Larry got the cutting torch and burned the bars through. With breaths held tight and chests constricted with excitement, Larry threw back the lid. The chest was packed tightly with heavy canvas bags, each one wired at the mouth, with a lead seal on the wire marked with the coat-of-arms of Spain. His hands trembling, Larry took hold of one of the bags and lifted. The rotted canvas broke, and dirty coins spilled into the chest, a few dropping to the deck.

Perhaps you've wondered how it feels to dip your hands into hundreds of thousands of dollars worth of precious metal? Well, Larry knew now, and the others too. It feels slippery, slimy, green with mold. It's heavy, it smells bad—and it is, to be honest, a wonderful sensation!

Larry leaned forward, his mind whirling, polishing one of the coins till the golden luster shone through the mold. Suddenly he felt faint. There was an itching and burning sensation on his skin, and dull pains in his muscles and joints. Chris looked at him sharply. A mottled rash was spreading over Larry's skin.

"Larry's got the bends," he gasped. "Open the recompression chamber, Peter, quickly." The treasure was forgotten by everyone but Smitty as Larry was helped over to the cylindrical chamber. The pain was increasing rapidly as Larry crawled in the chamber. The door was closed and the hiss of compressed air began.

All pain and nausea—the penalty for surfacing too fast—quickly left him as the compression built up. Chris' anxious face peered in through the glass port. Larry grinned self-consciously, and waved to show that he was all right.

CHAPTER 26

~~~~~~

Fortunately, Larry had only a light case of bends. Compressed air was forced into the recompression chamber till the air pressure was equal to that of the deck of the *Dona Isabella* where he had been working. Then the air pressure in the chamber was gradually reduced, just as it would have been if he had made the normal slow ascent through the water. The nitrogen which had dissolved in his blood stream under compression thus gradually passed off as compression was reduced. Seven hours after his collapse, the door was opened, and Larry wiggled out. He felt tired, but otherwise all right.

Larry was tempted to tease the others as he lay resting on a mattress while they sweated to get the anchor up, but decided he'd better not. He had helped bring on the attack himself by his own foolishness, and he knew what a hard, dirty, interminable job it was to crank those endless anchor chains up inch by inch on the windlass.

With the engine purring smoothly, the *Jolly Roger* headed for Borinquen Point and San Juan, while they opened the other three chests. All were crammed with gold. Smitty expertly blew open the huge safe, a fascinating procedure to watch, and probably one of the few times in history a safe-cracker practiced his illegal art before an audience. The safe contained innumerable packages, most of them apparently jewels or packets of paper money which had practically disintegrated.

"How much do you suppose the treasure is worth?" Linda Currier asked her father.

Mr. Currier engaged in some mental arithmetic. "There must be close to two million dollars worth of gold," he finally said, "maybe more. There's no way of telling how much the jewels are worth until we get an appraisal. The tax collector will be very glad to appraise them for us!"

"We have to give half of the treasure to the government, don't we?" asked Larry. Mrs. Cahill laughed. "Don't be so greedy, Larry. There'll be enough left for all of us."

"What d'ya want to declare it for?" snarled Smitty. "Why not just sail off with the whole lot of it?"

They stared coldly at Smitty. If any of them might have been tempted to conceal the treasure, the look of savage greed on Smitty's face would have changed their minds.

"Because it's the law," said Chris. "Because it's right. And because we don't operate crookedly—having to hide and lie and perjure ourselves. That's why."

"I'm entitled to a share. A full share," declared Smitty angrily. "You never would have got the treasure if I hadn't told you how to do it."

"We could have cut it open without you," said Chris. "It would have taken longer, that's all. For that matter, we could salvage the whole cargo of the ship, if we wanted to get heavy equipment. We'd only have to put lifting cables around her, attached to pontoons, lift her off the bottom, and float her in by successive stages to shallow water. Leapfrog her in. You'll get a share, but we haven't decided yet how much."

Smitty went off to sulk in the bow. Mr. Currier remarked: "Smitty doesn't really believe that anyone can be honest or sincere or unselfish. He's like a tone-deaf man with music; the evidence of his own senses is that there is no beauty or enjoyment to be found in music, and he has a constant suspicion that there's a conspiracy of some kind to deceive him that music can be enjoyable." He paused and regarded the treasure chests thoughtfully. "As a matter of fact, the government may not demand half of the treasure."

"I thought that was the automatic rule," said Chris. "Half of the treasure to the government."

"That was the old medieval law," explained Mr. Currier. "Half of any treasure trove went to the sovereign. But in the United States, the Secretary of the Treasury can make whatever division he wishes. The law says he can make any agreement he deems 'just and reasonable.' Generally, he takes into consideration how much time and money and risk it took to recover the treasure. In some cases, the government has let the finder keep 75 per cent —in one case, even 90 per cent. We'll get at least half, and I think probably more, since the government apparently didn't even know of the existence of the *Dona Isabella*. In any case, we're all rich."

Yes, they had gold, and silver too. They looked at it, counted it, played with it. It was wonderful . . . But the odd thing was how quickly they got used to it—not in weeks or days, but in hours.

Night was falling as the *Jolly Roger* passed into San Juan harbor, under El Morro's three grim tiers of threatening batteries that face the Atlantic with such Spanish bravado. Here indeed were the frowning bastions of the

Spanish Main, reeking with memories of treachery, in-
trigue, and the sheen of steel; of conquistadores and can-
nibals; of slaves and slavers and slim pirate galleys. They
sailed past the old harbor, which from a low-lying craft
like the *Jolly Roger* had even greater allure than when
seen from ashore. Walls and towers took on new proportions, perspective was shortened, altitudes lengthened. So
the city had looked when the great treasure galleons sheltered in this very spot from the piratical fleet of Sir Fran-
cis Drake.

They passed the skyscrapers of the modern waterfront section, the Coast Guard base, and in to the quay in
the inner harbor or marina. Chief Maddox had seen them
sail in, had raced to the waterfront in a jeep, and was
standing by to take a line as they worked the *Jolly Roger*
in between two of the inter-island trading schooners.
There was much excitement on the schooners and along
the waterfront, for no one in San Juan ever before had
seen a craft of the *Jolly Roger's* graceful build.

Chief Maddox was granted a quick, cautious peek at
the treasure chests, which were covered with tarpaulins
and tied around with heavy lines. They had another visi-
tor, too; José Figueroa, the newsboy who had trailed the
Wrangler's crew for them a short time ago, though it
seemed ages since that day when they had first visited San
Juan and the *Dona Isabella's* treasure was still only a vague,
unrealized dream.

They didn't mention the treasure in front of José,
which was a relief. There comes a time when you've got
to stop talking and thinking about money, and making
grandiose plans for travelling and adventure and spend-
ing. One of the sudden, heavy rain squalls common to the
islands of the trade wind belt drove them below to the
cabin. They sat around the cabin table, joking with José
and Chief Maddox, secretly relieved not to be talking

about treasure, though one or another of them was constantly jumping up to look through the port-light to be sure it was still there. They were all too tense to think of sleep until the chests had been turned over to the Insular Office of the Treasury Department. They planned to call at the office as soon as it opened in the morning.

There was a sudden crash against the side of the *Jolly Roger*, followed by a succession of bumps. Then the pound of feet on the deck. Nimble little José was the first one out of the companionway. As he emerged, he was grasped by a pair of rough hands, lifted and carried bodily to the rail, and thrown on the cobbles of the quay.

Larry, Chris, Maddox and the others were on deck before the boarders could clap the scuttle closed. The *Wrangler* was lashed to the *Jolly Roger's* outboard side, her crew moving swiftly to the attack. Other dark forms were leaping aboard from the dock. Their enemies had acquired reinforcements for this last desperate attempt at the treasure of the *Dona Isabella*. Larry drove his fist into a pallid blob of a face shining in the wet darkness, then was briefly disabled by a sharp kick in the groin. Chris and Peter were calling for the police, but the roar of thunder and the drum of the pelting rain drowned out their calls. The usual dock loungers had been driven to shelter by the storm so there was no one to hear. Chief Maddox, bellowing with rage, was swinging his big fists like sledge hammers. Several dark forms sprawled unconscious on the deck as proof that casualties had occurred. It was impossible to tell friend from foe in the blackness. One lightning flash revealed to Larry two strangers slugging away at one another. They grunted in astonishment as each recognized the other. Both turned on Larry, who ducked around the cabin and grabbed an oak belaying pin from the fife rail around the mainmast.

From the shore there suddenly came a shrill yelping,

and a succession of small forms bounded aboard. José had risen bruised and bleeding from the dock. Across the street from him, taking shelter from the rain, was a group of his fellow shoe-shine boys, who are as numerous in old San Juan as the sea gulls. *"Qué pasa?"* one of them had called out to José. That indomitable youngster yelled for help, and the whole crew of urchins charged like a pack of terriers. More were on the way, too; not only shoe-shine boys, but newsboys and the kids who hung around the docks diving for pennies thrown in the water by tourists.

The kids had a simple tactic. Two of them would trip or tackle someone on deck, and two others would fall on him. The spread-eagled adult was then held down, a boy on each leg and arm. The only difficulty was that they didn't know friend from foe, and Larry soon found himself lying helpless on the deck with the others. As the sounds of battle lessened, José ran around looking in the faces of the erstwhile combatants, ordering the release of the *Jolly Roger's* crew in staccato Spanish. Larry was allowed up, his four captors promptly falling on another prone struggling figure, which was almost smothered under the wiry bodies of eight youngsters wild with excitement and battle madness.

Then sirens wailed on shore, and the police riot squad arrived to take over the ship, the headlights of their cars shining over the deckload of squirming figures. Chief Maddox, his uniform torn and his knuckles bruised and bleeding, shouldered his way to the police lieutenant. Rapidly he explained the situation. The Chief was well known in San Juan, and his word was enough to separate the modern-day pirates from their intended victims.

CHAPTER 27

Now it was over. The treasure was safe ashore, and lawyers and tax-collectors were already arguing between themselves about it. There was a perceptible feeling of let-down, almost of regret that the treasure had been recovered, and that those high moments of blended skill and fear were memories.

Then Chris and Mona made a not unexpected announcement. Chris had asked Mr. Currier if he would agree to his marriage to Mona. Mr. Currier was delighted, provided Mona would consent, but that maiden had secretly settled on Chris for her husband even before they had left Florida. All that had remained was for Chris to discover his good fortune.

After the congratulations were over, there was much planning for the future. Chris and Peter thought they'd like to go into large-scale commercial salvaging, now that they had ample capital. Mr. Currier intended to buy back his family's ancestral sugar central, and he invited Mrs. Cahill and Larry to stay with him and with Linda.

Larry felt left out of things. Chris and Peter had not included him in their plans. "What am I," he inquired bitterly, "an orphan?"

Chris laughed. "Other people will be making plans for you, my boy. Do you realize how old you are? Have you ever heard of the draft board? Peter and I want you in with us, naturally, but first you've got a spell to put in for Uncle Sam."

Chief Maddox, who was visiting them again—he being now almost a member of the family—edged his chair closer to Larry. "What branch of the service are you going in?" he asked.

"I hadn't thought much about it, Chief," answered Larry. "There's been so much going on." They all laughed. "I'll probably enlist in the Coast Guard or in the Navy," continued Larry. Chief Maddox leaned closer still. "You'll have to earn a Chief's rating before you can dive in the Navy. Join the Coast Guard here, and I'll guarantee you can go on with your diving. If you enlist here in Puerto Rico, you may be able to do part of your tour of duty right here where Chris did, and where your friends and family are."

"What do you think?" Larry asked Linda.

"I think it's the most wonderful idea in the world," answered Linda, "provided Chief Maddox can guarantee that you'll be assigned to Puerto Rico." She looked expectantly at the Chief.

Maddox laughed. "I told you before, a Chief Boatswain's Mate isn't the same thing as an Admiral. No one can guarantee anything. But I've been in this game and I'll tell you one little thing. In a matter like this, you're better off having a Chief working for you than an Admiral. Petty officers handle the actual assignments, and we've got ways." He laughed again. "I think it can be arranged, kids."

There's nothing much else to tell. Oh yes, the shoe-shine boys and newsboys of San Juan now have a thriving baseball league—"beisball," they call it, with uniforms and equipment that wouldn't shame a major league club. The petty officers' mess at the Coast Guard base in San Juan has certain little luxuries which the officers' club might envy. All paid for by certain anonymous civilian benefactors.

Smitty? They never had to decide how big a share to grant that slippery individual. He had secretly dipped into the treasure chests, and helped himself to all the gold he could carry. Chris laughed at this, for the share he would probably have been granted would have been worth more than the value of the gold he stole, the yellow metal being heavy stuff, and Smitty not a robust person. Larry was delighted with this ending, for, as he said, it brought the parallel with his favorite story, *Treasure Island,* to a fitting climax. Had not Long John Silver also escaped from the Hispaniola with a pocketful of gold?

GLOSSARY

Agar
Salt water alfalfa used for medicines.

Air control valve
Valve for admitting fresh air to helmet, and controlling air pressure inside.

Air embolism
Air bubbles collecting at heart or brain because lung pressure is higher than outside pressure.

Air regulating exhaust valve
Valve that lets out used air from diver's helmet, and controls pressure inside helmet.

Aqua lung
Air tank and breathing mask used in skin diving.

Atmosphere of pressure
Unit of air pressure equal to normal atmospheric pressure; 14.7 pounds per square inch.

Automatic air escape
An automatic valve to prevent excessive pressure in diver's dress and helmet.

Balloon
Letting diving dress fill with air, so diver floats to surface.

Barometric pressure
The pressure of the atmosphere, which affects weather.

Beam ends
When boat heels over till deck is in water, she is sailing on her beam ends.

Bearing
Compass direction of an object from a ship's course.

Bends	Slang for caisson disease; caused by nitrogen dissolving in blood stream of diver.
Bower anchor	Light anchor used for temporary anchoring.
Branch pipe	Pipe from which mud sucked up by dredge line is spilled out.
Bridle	Rope or wire, the end of which is in two pieces like a backwards "V."
Bugeye	Sailboat with overhanging bow, and two masts which lean far backwards.
Bullion	Uncoined gold and silver.
Buoyancy	Relation of weight to water displaced.
Buzzer	Telephone signal in diver's helmet.
Caisson disease	Sickness caused by nitrogen dissolving in a diver's blood. Results from surfacing too fast.
Capstan	A vertical drum on deck of ship for hoisting or pulling heavy weights.
Carbon dioxide	A gas exhaled after the lungs have used up the oxygen in the air inhaled.
Carbon monoxide	Poisonous gas from exhaust of a gas engine.
Check valve	Valve which lets air pass in only one direction.
Chinook	Name given a warm, moist southwest wind.
Clamshell bucket	A big hoisting bucket shaped like a clam shell.

Claustrophobia	Fear of being enclosed or confined in a small area.
Clinker-built	Boat with overlapping planks.
Compressed air illness	Disease caused by nitrogen bubbles dissolved in the blood stream.
Compressor	An engine which compresses or squeezes air to put it under pressure.
Compressor exhaust	Poisonous gases from exhaust of motor.
Compressor intake	Place where motor draws in air.
Con	To direct the steering of a boat.
Corselet	Breastplate to which diver's helmet is attached.
Coupling	Fastening for putting together short pieces of hose.
Crane barge	A large, clumsy squared-off boat having a crane or derrick for hoisting heavy objects.
Deadeye	A flat circular piece of wood with three holes, used for tightening a ship's rigging.
Decompress	To reduce air pressure.
Decompression	Gradual reduction of a diver's air pressure, to let nitrogen dissolve slowly.
Decompression chamber	A compartment in which air pressure can be built up for gradual decompression after a diver has come up too fast.

Decompression stage	A platform on which a diver stands while he is being hoisted up gradually to decompress.
Demand valve	A valve which lets in just enough air for a diver.
Descending line	A rope used by a diver in descending, which also marks the proper spot to begin going up.
Displacement	The weight of water displaced by an object in water, like a ship or a diver.
Distance line	A rope used by a diver to keep from getting lost on the bottom.
Diving stage	A platform on which divers sometimes stand in descending and ascending.
Dredge line	A suction hose to suck up mud and silt.
Dredge (suction)	A suction pump which sucks up mud through a hose or pipe.
Dry rot	Rotten timbers in a ship, caused by lack of ventilation.
Exhaust valve	Valve which lets used air out of a diver's helmet, and controls pressure inside.
Faceplate	Hinged front window in diver's helmet.
Fathom	Six feet.
Fidley	Part of deck over steamship's boilers, through which funnel or smokestack passes.

Fife rail	A rail around a mast with holes for belaying pins.
Flotsam	Floating wreckage.
Frigate	In old times, a three-masted warship with square sails.
Galleon	An ancient form of ship, with many decks rising in stern.
Galley	A ship's kitchen.
Gelignite	High explosive.
Grab bucket	A large self-closing bucket to pick up heavy objects.
Grouting	A form of cementing—using concrete under water.
Hance irons	Iron braces for bulwarks of boat.
Hawse holes	Holes in a ship's bows through which anchor cable passes.
Hawsers	Very heavy ropes used for towing or fastening a ship.
Heel	When a boat leans over, as from pressure of wind.
Helium	A gas sometimes used instead of nitrogen in the compressed air a diver breathes.
Helmet	Large dome-shaped object with glass windows, which covers a diver's head.
Helmet cushion	A cushion to relieve pressure of helmet weight, and to help seal out water.
Ingots	Small bars of metal.

Jacob's ladder	A ladder with wooden steps and side ropes.
Jet hose	Pressure hose used in jetting.
Jetting	Using water under pressure to wash away sand and mud.
Jettison	Objects thrown off a ship to lighten it.
Knot	Unit of speed for a boat; one nautical mile per hour.
Lee	The side of a boat away from the wind; a lee shore is a shore toward which the wind is blowing.
Life line	Rope used to lower or hoist diver. Often has telephone cable inside.
Lighter	A small barge into which cargo is loaded.
Log	A written record of a ship's voyage or of a diver's dive.
Maelstrom	Water moving rapidly in a circle.
Make fast	To belay or fasten down a rope.
Making (flood)	Tide is coming in.
Moray	A large, vicious eel.
Mushroom	A very heavy anchor used when a boat doesn't move around much, and seldom has to hoist it up.
Negative buoyancy	Heavier than the water the diver displaces, so he sinks.
Neophyte	Beginner.
Nitrogen	A gas which comprises ⅘ of the air.

Octopus	A marine animal with soft oval body and eight long arms with suction cups.
Ordnance	Various kinds of cannon.
Oxygen poisoning	A sickness like pneumonia, caused by breathing too much oxygen when under pressure.
Oxy-helium diving	A diver breathing oxygen and helium instead of compressed air.
Pneumatic tools	Tools powered by compressed air.
Pontoons	Floats which can be filled with water and fastened to a sunken object. Compressed air forces out the water, and they rise, bringing up the sunken object with them.
Port	The left side of a ship, as you face forward.
Port lights	Circular windows in a ship.
Positive buoyancy	Weighing less than the water displaced; enough air in a diver's suit to allow him to float.
Privateer	A privately owned warship.
Puncheon (rum)	A heavy cask or barrel used to hold liquor.
Purser	The business manager on a ship; the man who would have direct charge of any valuable cargo.
Quay	A dock or wharf that is parallel to the shore.
Raft booms	Floating rafts of loose logs confined by

	other logs chained together on the edges.
Reef	To reduce the area of a sail exposed to the wind by folding in and tieing down the lower edge.
Reservoir (air)	A tank into which compressed air is forced, to be used by a diver.
Salvage	The act of saving a ship or cargo from the ocean; also legal claim against owner by someone who has saved it.
Schooner	Two-masted sailing vessel, usually with rear mast taller than front mast, except on a bugeye. Sometimes has more than two masts.
Securing pin	A pin on a deep sea diver's helmet which keeps the lock from coming loose.
Self-contained diving outfit	A diving rig with which the diver carries his own air supply in tanks on his back.
Shanghai	To kidnap a person to make him work on a ship.
Sheet	A rope used to control the angle of a sail to the wind. It is not a sail.
Shoal	Shallow—not deep.
Shot line	A line with heavy weight on end, dropped from a diving boat, used to guide the diver on his descent and ascent.
Skin diving	Diving with breathing mask, but with bathing suit instead of diving dress.

Slack	Loose.
Slag	Molten metal.
Slip	A space between two piers for tieing up a boat.
Sloop	A single-masted sailboat with one sail in back of the mast and one or more in front of the mast.
Snorkel	A device for breathing while just under the surface of the water through a tube extending above the water.
Spindrift	See Spray . . . water blown from crest of waves by strong wind.
Spume	Foam and froth caused on water by strong wind.
Squall	Sudden, short storm that comes up without warning.
Square rigger	An old-fashioned sailing ship whose sails extend crosswise to the deck instead of lengthwise.
Squeeze	Pressure inside a diving dress, lower than outside pressure of water and forcing the diver up into his rigid helmet.
Starboard	The right side of a ship as you face forward.
Storm warnings	A system of flags flown by lighthouses, Coast Guard stations, etc., warning of approaching storm.
Strangulation	Inability to breathe. For a diver, when air stops coming, or water rises in helmet over nose and mouth.

Sugar central	A sugar cane plantation and factory where cane is made into molasses and sugar.
Surge	A large swelling wave which can lift a diving boat so high the lines pull on the diver.
Tackle	A combination of ropes and blocks or pulleys that multiplies power.
Tarpaulin	A heavy canvas used to cover and protect cargo hatches and other objects.
Tender	The man who stays on a diving boat or barge and tends the diver's lines, air compressor, etc.
Teredos (ship-worms)	Tapelike worms that eat into wood that is under water.
Tompion	A plug fitted in a cannon's mouth, to protect the inside from moisture.
Trunion	Protruding part of cannon for supporting it on its carriage.
Twill	Strong cloth woven diagonally.
Ventilation	In diver's helmet, sufficient movement of air to provide oxygen for breathing and to carry off the used air the diver breathes out.
Wahoo	Tropical fish.
Watches	Division of a ship's crew into groups, each group being on duty in turn for a fixed number of hours.
Weather	The side of a ship that is exposed to the wind.

Winch	A hoisting or pulling machine with a horizontal drum.
Windlass	A machine for cranking up a heavy anchor.
Windward	In the direction from which the wind is coming.
Yaw	A sudden sidewise lurch of a ship's stern, very dangerous in a heavy sea.
Yawl boat	A heavy lifeboat and utility boat usually carried on davits across a larger boat's stern. Generally has a motor.